MW00398963

A GUIDEBOOK TO
FORTRAN ON
SUPERCOMPUTERS

A GUIDEBOOK TO
FORTRAN ON
SUPERCOMPUTERS

John M. Levesque
Pacific-Sierra Research Corporation, Placerville, California

Joel W. Williamson
Pacific-Sierra Research Corporation, Placerville, California

Academic Press, Inc.

Harcourt Brace Jovanovich, Publishers
San Diego   New York   Berkeley   Boston
London   Sydney   Tokyo   Toronto

We dedicate this Book
To Charles Babbage who thought up the computer,
To Augusta Ada Byron who taught us all how to program,
To Herman Hollerith without whom we wouldn't have (been) counted,
To John von Neumann who taught us how to do one thing at a time,
To Seymour Cray who showed us how to do everything at once.

ACADEMIC PRESS, INC.
San Diego, California 92101

United Kingdom Edition published by
ACADEMIC PRESS, INC. (LONDON) LTD.
24-28 Oval Road, London NW1 7DX

Library of Congress Cataloging-in-Publication Data

Levesque, John M.
    A guidebook to Fortran on supercomputers / John M. Levesque, Joel
W. Williamson
        p.   cm.
    Includes index.
    ISBN 0-12-444760-0 (alk. paper)
    1. FORTRAN (Computer program language) 2. Supercomputers-
-Programming.   I. Williamson, Joel W.   II. Title.
QA76.73.F25L475   1988
005.2'1—dc19   88-14129
                                                          CIP

PRINTED IN THE UNITED STATES OF AMERICA
    90 91   9 8 7 6 5 4 3

CONTENTS

PREFACE

Fortran is the dominant language used on supercomputers today, and the vendors of these machines have expended much effort in providing optimizing compilers for Fortran programs. However, many constructs in existing programs prevent the compilers from generating optimized code. On a supercomputer, fully optimized code can run an order of magnitude faster than unoptimized, so it is imperative that a programmer understand how to write Fortran in a way that realizes the full potential of the target machine.

This book, the first of its kind, explains in detail both the underlying architecture of today's supercomputers and the manner by which a compiler maps Fortran code onto that architecture. Most important, the constructs preventing full optimizations are outlined, and specific strategies for restructuring a program are provided.

This book is based on the authors' actual experience in restructuring existing programs for particular supercomputers and generally follows the format of a series of supercomputer seminars that they regularly present on a worldwide basis. All examples are explained with actual Fortran code; no mathematical abstractions such as dataflow graphs are used. Targeted for programmers directly involved in optimizing Fortran programs on today's high-performance scientific computers, the book also provides excellent preparation for anyone interested in the field.

Chapter 1 is an introduction to the basic concepts of scalar, vector, and parallel processing. Chapter 2 provides an in-depth look at the architectural features of a variety of existing machines, with particular attention paid to the features common to many of them. Chapter 3 explains the optimization techniques used by compilers and how a programmer can take advantage of this knowledge both in restructuring existing programs and in the development of new applications. Chapter 4 presents dozens of examples of loops from real-world programs, with a discussion of the inherent problems, and a restructured version that typically runs two to twenty times faster than the original. Performance of both the original and restructured code is graphed for each loop. A list of common abbreviations and glossary of important terms are provided in Appendix A.

The authors acknowledge the many contributions of their students over the years. Special thanks go to our employer, Pacific-Sierra Research Corporation, for all of its support in this endeavor, to Mark Koenig, who prepared the many figures in the text, to Tracey Andersen, who transcribed several rough drafts, and to Gene Wagenbreth, who carefully read the original manuscript and made many fine suggestions. Any errors and omissions are solely the responsibility of the authors.

1

INTRODUCTION

This book is concerned with the effective use of the Fortran programming language on a loosely defined class of machines known as supercomputers. It is assumed that the reader has a working knowledge of Fortran. As for knowledge of supercomputers, it is assumed that the reader's principal programming experience has been on the classical "von Neumann" machines: sequential, scalar processors. Why make such an assumption? Because the von Neumann machines number in the millions, but the supercomputers number in the hundreds; because until recently only a few universities have had access to supercomputers, and this access was often restricted to a small group of researchers; in short, because most of us grew up on conventional computers.

1.1
CONVENTIONAL COMPUTERS

In describing his surgical skills, Charles Emerson Winchester of the television series M*A*S*H once claimed: "I do one thing at a time, I do it very well, and then I move on." This is the essence of the "von Neumann" architecture of a conventional computer, and it also well describes the approach taken by many programmers in the use of Fortran. Standard Fortran, in fact, demands such an approach. Even when operating on an entire array of numbers, we must specify what is to be done to a single array element, then loop through all the subscripts of all the dimensions of the array. Thus (until ANSI 8X becomes the Fortran standard) we are forced to transform the matrix algebra

1

statement:

$$A = B + C$$

into

```
      DO 1000 J = 1, NDIM2
        DO 1000 I = 1, NDIM1
          A(I,J) = B(I,J) + C(I,J)
   1000 CONTINUE
```

Most of us have learned to work within the constraints of Fortran over the years, and many know that it is more efficient on a conventional computer to write the matrix sum as we have done, rather than with the J and I loops reversed:

```
      DO 1010 I = 1, NDIM1
        DO 1010 J = 1, NDIM2
          A(I,J) = B(I,J) + C(I,J)
   1010 CONTINUE
```

How much more efficient? Maybe 10%, 20%, 50%; certainly less than a factor of two. For many programmers, the payoff for writing efficient Fortran for conventional computers has not been high enough to warrant their attention. However, as we will soon learn — on a supercomputer, depending on the dimensions of the arrays — loop 1000 may execute an order of magnitude faster than loop 1010.

1.2
WHAT'S A SUPERCOMPUTER ANYWAY?

Time was invented to keep everything from happening all at once.

—Anonymous

Supercomputers are built in direct defiance of the preceding statement. A survey of the literature will reveal no rigorous definition of a supercomputer, nor do we intend to give one here. One popular working notion is that a supercomputer is the biggest, fastest computer available at the moment. This, of course, limits the class to one computer at a time, assuming we could get all interested parties to agree on which one — probably a hopeless task.

Since this book is about Fortran, we will limit our discussion to the so-called "scientific" computers as opposed to those used primarily for business data processing, although we acknowledge that there is often a significant overlap. There are certainly some very big, fast scientific computers, some with physical memories exceeding two billion bytes (gigabytes), some with clock cycles close to four nanoseconds. (A nanosecond [nsec] is one billionth of a second.)

These computers can be programmed to perform in a conventional manner, and they will still be faster than other computers just because their clocks are so much faster. What distinguishes the supercomputers from others is their ability to perform many operations simultaneously. To paraphrase Charles Emerson Winchester, supercomputers "do many things at once, do them very well, and then they move on."

Some supercomputers accomplish many simultaneous operations by "vector" processing, that is, by using powerful instructions to feed arrays of operands through a "pipeline" or assembly line of operations. This pipeline concept is a streamlining of the conventional scalar processor, a recognition that the most intense use of a computer is almost always in a loop, doing the same operations to many different operands. The Cray Research, Inc. (CRI) Cray-1S, X-MP, Cray-2, the Control Data Corporation (CDC) CYBER 205 and ETA 10, the IBM 3090 Vector Facility, the Fujitsu VP Series, the Nippon Electric (NEC) SX2 series, and the Hitachi S-810 and S-820 are all examples of pipelined vector processors.

Other supercomputers accomplish many simultaneous operations by having many processors working in parallel on a program. The most famous is the ILLIAC IV, recently decommissioned by the NASA Ames Research Laboratory. Other parallel machines are INTEL's iPSC; NCUBE's NCUBE/n series; Bolt, Beranek and Newman's BUTTERFLY; Floating Point System's T-Series; and Thinking Machines' Connection Machine. Of course some machines combine both parallel and vector architectures, even some of the computers already mentioned, such as the Cray X-MP.

Finally, in recent years there have appeared some machines classified as "minisupercomputers." These machines incorporate many of the architectural features of the supercomputers but use slower electronic components and generally smaller memories. Typical clock speeds are from 50 to 200 nanoseconds, and physical memory sizes range up to hundreds of megabytes (millions of bytes). The Alliant FX/1 and FX/8, Convex C-1 and C-MP, ELXSI 6400, and Scientific Computer Systems SCS-40 are all members of this class of machines.

All of the supercomputers and minisupercomputers are characterized by their ability to perform much faster in "vector" or "parallel" mode than in "scalar" mode. The performance might be from two to one thousand times faster, but only if we know how to program them. That is what this book is about, the effective use of Fortran on supercomputers.

1.3
TERMINOLOGY

We assume that the reader is familiar with many of the basic terms describing computers and computer languages. But certain common words have special meanings in the discussion of parallel and vector computers. We wish to introduce just a few of them here.

1.3.1   Scalar

A scalar value is a single value or entity. A scalar instruction operates on one or a pair of scalar values, as in the Fortran statement:

```
SCA1 = SCA2 + SCA3
```

At least four scalar instructions must be executed to complete this statement: two fetch instructions to get the values of SCA2 and SCA3 from memory, an add instruction, and a store instruction to place the answer into SCA1 in memory. Conventional computers execute DO loops in scalar mode. Consider:

```
      DO 1020 I = 1, 100
         ARRAY1(I) = ARRAY2(I) + ARRAY3(I)
 1020 CONTINUE
```

This loop requires the execution of at least 400 scalar instructions to perform the desired addition of ARRAY2 and ARRAY3.

1.3.2   Vector and Stride

Physicists, engineers, and linear algebra buffs: Suspend your long-held notions of vectors. A vector is an ordered list of scalar values, and it is inherently one-dimensional. A simple vector in a computer's memory is defined as having a *starting address,* a *length* (number of elements), and a *stride* (constant distance in memory between elements). All vector processors have machine instructions that allow the fetching and storing of vectors of values from memory. Consider again:

```
      DO 1020 I = 1, 100
         ARRAY1(I) = ARRAY2(I) + ARRAY3(I)
 1020 CONTINUE
```

On a vector processor, ARRAY1 can be regarded as a vector whose starting address is ARRAY1(1), whose length is 100, and whose stride is 1 (the increment of the DO loop index I). On the CYBER 205, execution of a single vector instruction can perform all of the operations of the entire DO 1020 loop. So a vector instruction performs its operation on each of the elements of its vector operands. It is important to note that a vector instruction does not operate on all of the vector elements simultaneously. Rather, the pairs of operands are fed into the pipelined vector processor in a continuous stream, with the results flowing out and back to memory in a continuous stream, but still one at a time. Depending on the machine and the vector length of the operation, this streamlining produces results at a rate 2 to 100 times faster than if scalar instructions were used. When vector operations can be used to perform a computation, it is said to be "vectorized." (A full discussion of simple and more complicated vectors can be found in Chapter 3.)

1.3.3 Parallel and Concurrent

These terms are synonymous when applied to computers, and they always mean the simultaneous execution of instructions within a given machine. There are, however, many nuances. Many scalar processors have some degree of parallelism on a fine-grain level. If the central processing unit (CPU) possesses entirely independent add and multiply units, then it is possible in the execution of the statement

```
PARTY = CHIPS * DIP + PEOPLE + SONG
```

that the sum of PEOPLE + SONG can be computed in parallel with the product CHIPS * DIP.

Most vector processors can also issue vector instructions in parallel, but the most interesting application of the idea of concurrency is on a multiprocessor system — that is, a computer with more than one CPU. Consider, one more time with feeling:

```
       DO 1020 I = 1, 100
          ARRAY1(I) = ARRAY2(I) + ARRAY3(I)
 1020 CONTINUE
```

On a parallel computer with 100 processors, each iteration of this loop could be assigned to its own processor. That is, Processor 1 is assigned the task of computing

```
ARRAY1(1) = ARRAY2(1) + ARRAY3(1)
```

Processor 2 computes

```
ARRAY1(2) = ARRAY2(2) + ARRAY3(2)
```

and so forth. The beauty of this scheme is that the loop runs 100 times faster than if it were executed on a single processor. This statement ignores any cost of initializing parallel execution. This and other practical considerations will be discussed in later sections.

1.4
AMDAHL'S LAW

Amdahl's law states that in any system having two or more processing modes of differing speeds, the performance of the system will be dominated by the slowest mode. This has immediate application to vector and parallel computers.

1.4.1 Amdahl's Law for Vector Processors

Here we are concerned with computer systems having scalar processing as well as vector processing. Since vector processing is inherently faster than scalar, Amdahl's law tells us that the system will be dominated by scalar performance. The following is a derivation of computer performance as a function of the fraction of code vectorized. Let

Ts = the time required to perform an operation in scalar mode
Tv = the time required to perform an operation in vector mode
Fs = the fraction of operations performed in scalar mode
Fv = the fraction of operations performed in vector mode

Then the time T to perform N operations is

$$T = N \cdot (Fs \cdot Ts + Fv \cdot Tv)$$

Given that $Fs + Fv = 1$, then

$$T = N \cdot [(1 - Fv) \cdot Ts + Fv \cdot Tv]$$

Normalizing to $Ts = 1$ and defining vector speedup:

$$VS = \frac{Ts}{Tv}$$

then

$$T = N \cdot \left[(1 - Fv) + \frac{Fv}{VS} \right]$$

$$= N \cdot \left[1 - \frac{(VS - 1)}{VS} \cdot Fv \right]$$

Now let performance be defined as the number of operations performed per unit time:

$$P = \frac{N}{T}$$

$$P = \frac{1}{\left[1 - \frac{(VS - 1)}{VS} \cdot Fv \right]}$$

This provides performance as a function of the fraction of operations vectorized and allows us to determine for an existing program how much code must be vectorized to achieve performance goals. Figure 1.1 is a graph of this function of $VS = 10$ (typical of the Cray X-MP computers).

Note how this graph shows that the performance of a vector processor is dominated by its scalar processing capability. One-hundred percent vectorized produces a factor of 10 performance improvement, but 55% vectorized is only a factor of 2! Not until 90% is vectorized does performance exceed one-half of the maximum.

Note that the abscissa is labeled "Fraction of *Utilized* Code Vectorized." Fortunately, most programs follow an 80–20 rule, that is, 80% of the time is spent in 20% of the code. It might be 90–10 or 75–25, but most programs

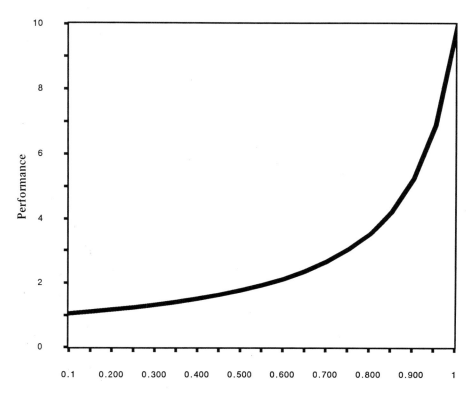

Fraction of Utilized Code Vectorized

FIGURE 1.1.
Amdahl's Law for Vector Processors

have a few very CPU-intensive routines. It is conceivable that a program of 50,000 statements would have a solution routine of 100 statements in which 80% of the CPU time is spent. The point is that if the solution routine is vectorized, then 80% of the *utilized* code is vectorized, even though only 0.2% of the statements have been vectorized.

One of the important lessons to learn from this graph of Amdahl's law is that in benchmarking a typical mix of applications programs in which fraction of vectorization is about 0.5, the machine with the best scalar processing performance is probably going to win. To drive the point home, imagine a hypothetical computer that performs vector operations in zero time but whose scalar performance is one-half that graphed in Figure 1.1. Note that in the equation for performance, the term $(VS -1)/VS$ goes to one as VS goes to infinity. Superimposing the hypothetical performance with the original, we have Figure 1.2.

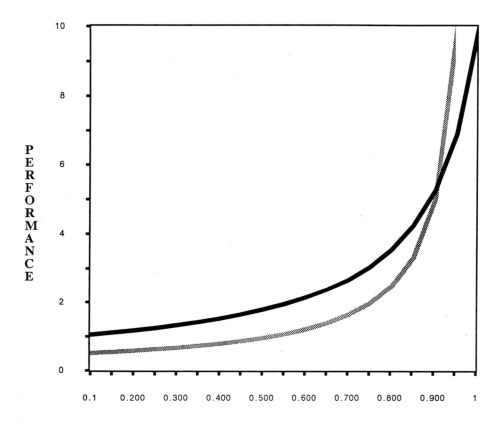

FRACTION OF UTILIZED CODE VECTORIZED
FIGURE 1.2.
Amdahl's Law with Zero-Time Vector Processor

Even though the hypothetical computer has an *infinite* vector performance, it does not outperform the original (real) computer until vectorization
exceeds 90% — because of its lower scalar speed.

1.4.2 Amdahl's Law for Parallel Processors

Here we are concerned with machines that achieve their speedup over single
processor scalar performance by spreading the computation over many processors. If there were no cost to do this, then a linear speedup with number of
processors could be achieved, so this is the theoretical maximum performance of such a system. In the derivation, we show the effects of the overhead

time necessary to properly initiate and synchronize parallel processing, as well as the cost of using only one processor in critical regions of the program where parallel processing is not possible.

Ts = the time required to perform an operation on a single processor
Fs = fraction of operations performed on a single processor
Tp = the time required to perform an operation on M processors (Ts/M)
OH = the overhead for synchronizing parallel processors
Fp = fraction of code able to use M processors
NT = number of disjoint parallel tasks

Then the time to perform N operations is

$$T = N \cdot \left[Fs \cdot Ts + \sum_{i=1}^{NT} (Tp_i * Fp_i + OH_i) \right]$$

Normalizing to $Ts = 1$, then $Tp_i = 1/m_i$, and

$$T = N \left[Fs + \sum_{i=1}^{NT} \left(\frac{Fp_i}{m_i} + OH_i \right) \right]$$

where

$$Fs + \sum_{i=1}^{NT} Fp_i = 1$$

and m_i is the average number of processors used during the ith task.

The relationship is much more complex for multiprocessing; but, several important facts can be derived from the equation.

1. If we ignore overhead time and synchronization time and assume that all processors can be used on all tasks, then the upper bound for performance on a parallel processor is essentially the same relationship as for vector processing, that is

$$P = \frac{1}{\left(1 - \frac{(M-1)}{M} \cdot Fp \right)}$$

where M is the number of parallel processors, and Fp is the fraction of code able to use M processors. (The amount of code that can use parallel processing generally will be larger than the amount of code that can be vectorized.)

2. If the overhead time for initializing a task or synchronizing tasks is a significant fraction of the task time itself, then performance gain will be lost. Consider using 32 processors on a task of duration 1 sec. If

the overhead is on the order of 0.1 sec., the time for the task will be

$$T = \frac{1}{32} + .1 = 0.13 \text{ sec}$$

for an overall speedup factor of 8 rather than 32.

3. The most important fact that can be derived from this relationship is that the time spent using one processor has a dramatic effect on the overall run time. For example, if we only spend 1% of the overall time using one processor, the maximum speedup we can get over the performance of that one processor is 100—even if we have zero startup time and an infinite number of processors.

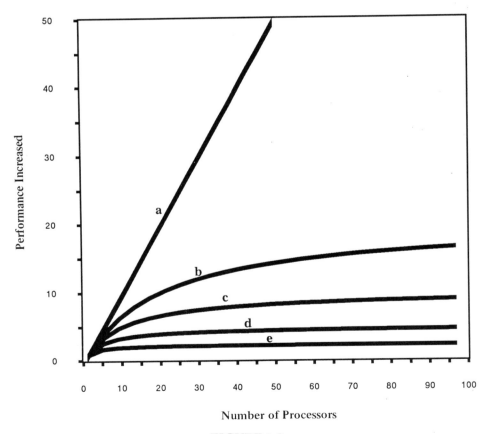

Number of Processors

FIGURE 1.3.
Performance of N Processors for Various Utilizations. Utilization:
a = 100%, b = 95%, c = 90%, d = 80%, e = 60%

Figure 1.3 depicts performance of a parallel system for several tasks with differing utilization of all processors. It should be clear from this that other-than-100% utilization leaves a significant number of processors idle for the duration of a task running on a many-processor system. For example, a task with 60% utilization cannot effectively use more than four processors.

1.5
SUMMARY

These basic notions of vector and parallel processing are central to the discussion that follows. Pipelining of operations and simultaneous execution of instructions are the mainstay of supercomputers. Learning how to realize them within the constraints of standard Fortran is the main thrust of this text.

Problems

1. When different supercomputers are compared, both scalar and vector performance must be considered. Amdahl's law plays an important role in estimating the relative performance differences of the machines. Derive an equation for calculating the performance of machine A over machine B as a function of vector speed of A, V_A, scalar speed of A, S_A, vector speed of B, V_B, and scalar speed of B, S_B. Hint: Use the fact that

$$\frac{\text{Performance of } A}{\text{Performance of } B} = \frac{\left(\dfrac{1}{T_A}\right)}{\left(\dfrac{1}{T_B}\right)}$$

   where

$$T_A = N \cdot \left(\frac{(1 - F_V)}{S_A} + \frac{F_V}{V_A}\right)$$

   and

$$T_B = N \cdot \left(\frac{(1 - F_V)}{S_B} + \frac{F_V}{V_B}\right)$$

2. Using the Formula derived in Problem 1, consider the following two machines:

	Scalar Speed	Vector Speed
Machine X	1 Mflop	1 Mflop
Machine Y	0.5 Mflop	20 Mflop

    a. Plot the performance ratio of machine Y to machine X for fraction of vectorization ranging from 0.0 to 1.0.

    b. How much vectorization is necessary for machine Y to run faster than machine X?

3. Amdahl's law can easily be extended to parallel machines. Derive the formula for performance ratio for parallel processors, analogous to that presented for vector processors in Problem 1. Consider also the following situations facing one who may want to upgrade from a uniprocessor to a massively parallel system:

	Relative Scalar Speed	Number of Processors
Machine X	1.0	1
Machine Y	0.1	1024

    a. Plot the performance ratio of machine Y to machine X for fraction of parallelization ranging from 0.0 to 1.0.

    b. How much parallelization is necessary for machine Y to run faster than machine X?

4. Using the formula from Problem 1, compare the following three machines.

    a. Which machine has the best performance for an application with no vectorization?

    b. Which machine is best for 100% vectorization?

    c. At what vectorization ratio do machines Y and Z have the same performance?

	Scalar Speed	Vector
Machine X	1	1
Machine Y	6	60
Machine Z	3	120

5. Things to try on your machine: Execute your code with full optimization and with no optimization. How much faster is the optimized than the unoptimized code? What fraction of your code has been vectorized or optimized automatically by the compiler?

2

SUPERCOMPUTER ARCHITECTURE

To achieve optimal performance on a supercomputer, it is essential for a Fortran programmer to understand the underlying architecture and instruction set of the target machine and how this architecture is utilized by the Fortran compiler. Without this understanding, seemingly harmless constructs used within a DO loop can dramatically affect the execution time of the loop. Consider the following two DO loops:

```
      DO 2000 I = 1,N            DO 2010 I = 1,N
         IF (A(I).GT.EPS) THEN      IF (A(I).GT.EPS) THEN
         AB = A(I) * B(I)
         X(I) = AB / Z(I)           X(I) = A(I) * B(I) / Z(I)
         Y(I) = Y(I) + AB           Y(I) = Y(I) + A(I) * B(I)
      ENDIF                      ENDIF
 2000 CONTINUE              2010 CONTINUE
```

Both of these loops store the same values into the X and Y arrays. However, the use of the scalar AB inside the IF-block of loop 2000 cannot be easily vectorized on some systems, because they are missing certain machine instructions found on others. (Use of scalars in DO loops is discussed fully in Chapter 3.)

2.1
BASIC FEATURES

Many of the important capabilities of supercomputers are evolutionary extensions of the features found on scalar processors, so a review of the development of these features can be instructive.

13

In the mid-1960s a start-up company named Control Data Corporation introduced a revolutionary new machine designated the 6600, partially designed by one of CDC's founders, Seymour Cray. Like many of today's minicomputers, the 6600 had a 100-nsec clock, fast registers, a large banked memory, and segmented functional units. The 6600 was the first major scientific computer to combine all of these features in a well-balanced system. In a sense it was the first supercomputer. We will examine each of these features as it relates to machine performance, and, where appropriate, trace its evolution through Seymour Cray's follow-on machines, the CDC 7600 and the Cray Research Cray-1 and Cray-2. In later sections we will see that many of these features can be found on the majority of commercially successful supercomputers and minisupercomputers.

2.1.1   Clock Cycle and Performance Measures

The clock cycle of a computer is the basic unit of time, and nothing (of interest to a Fortran programmer) happens in less than one clock cycle. If all other features of a computer system remain the same, then performance will vary inversely with the clock cycle. Recall from Chapter 1 that the clock cycle of a supercomputer is typically a small number of nanoseconds.

A computer can usually issue instructions at the maximum theoretical rate of one instruction per clock cycle. For example, the CDC 6600 had a clock cycle of 100 nsec and its inverse

$$\frac{1}{100 \times 10^{-9} \text{ sec}} = 10 \times 10^6$$

is the maximum number of instructions per second (ips) that the machine can issue. Because of the magnitude of the numbers involved, this rate is usually quoted in millions of instructions per second or "Mips." Thus the CDC 6600 can be rated at 10 Mips. Sometimes the *s* is dropped, so that we speak of a 10-Mip machine.

Reducing the clock cycle time has always been a goal of machine designers: the CDC 7600 had a clock cycle of 27.5 nanoseconds (36 Mips), and the Cray-1 has a clock cycle of 12.5 nanoseconds (80 Mips). Future designs are aiming for the 1-nsec clock cycle, which would provide a computer with a 1000-Mip rating.

Note that the Mip rating is the maximum *theoretical* instruction issue rate. Because of many different resource conflicts in the execution of a program, the *actual* issue rate is generally about one-tenth to one-half the theoretical maximum.

Because all supercomputers have features that generate many operations from the issuance of one instruction, the Mip rating of a supercomputer is of much less importance than it is for a conventional computer. As programmers, we are interested in how fast a computer can generate results in which we are interested. On conventional computers this is closely related to the rate instructions can be issued, and the maximum theoretical result rate then is one per clock cycle. The actual delivered result rate on a conventional computer is often a small fraction of the maximum. On a supercomputer the result rate is often more than one per clock cycle, much faster than the instruction issue rate. Since most scientific and engineering computation involves floating-point arithmetic, the performance measure for supercomputers used in preference to Mips is millions of floating-point operations per second, called "megaflops" or "Mflops." (When supercomputers are rated by their maximum theoretical result rate, this is known as "machoflops.")

2.1.2   Registers

Registers are a form of very high-speed memory used to hold the most heavily accessed information at any point in the execution of a program. They are necessarily expensive, and consequently there are not very many of them. There are generally three types of registers in a computer: 1) address registers that hold the locations of data within memory; 2) operand registers that hold the data items currently being manipulated by the program; and 3) an instruction stack, which is a set of registers holding the instructions in the part of the program currently being executed. On some computers a set of general-purpose registers is used to handle both address and operand computation.

Registers can generally provide their information to the CPU in one clock cycle, typically an order of magnitude faster than information can be fetched from memory to the CPU. It is up to the Fortran compiler to optimize its use of these registers, and in Chapter 3 we will learn how to help the compiler do just that.

Address Registers

The memory on a computer can be viewed as one large singly dimensioned array. All of our program variables and multidimensioned arrays are mapped into a piece of the computer's memory. At any point in our program, the compiler uses the address registers to compute the memory locations of the data items that currently need to be fetched and stored. Under certain circumstances the compiler might also use the address registers for some of our integer data arithmetic.

The 6600 and 7600 each have eight address registers named A0, A1, . . . A7 and eight backup registers B0, B1, . . . B7, which are used as a scratch pad for address calculations. The Cray-1 also has 8 A registers, but has 64 B registers.

For example, on a Cray, during execution of the Fortran statement

```
P(N) = 1.0
```

the value of N must be fetched from memory, placed in an A register, then added to the address of the array P decremented by one to compute the address of P(N). This is shown in Figure 2.1.

Operand Registers

As their name implies, these registers hold the current operands of the program during execution. In certain code segments there will be more operands than registers available to hold them. The compiler will optimize the use of the registers by retaining the most heavily used operands in the registers and assigning the least-used operands to temporary storage locations in memory.

The 6600 and 7600 each have eight operand registers named X0, X1, . . . , X7, which hold all of the operands and results during execution of the arithmetic and logical instructions of our program. The Cray-1 has eight registers, named S0, S1, . . . S7, which hold operands and results of *scalar* arithmetic operations. The S registers are backed up by 64 T registers used to hold intermediate results for later reference.

As a direct extension of the idea of scalar operand registers, the Cray-1 has eight *vector* operand registers, named V0, V1, . . . , V7. Each of these registers can hold up to 64 operands. A vector instruction to add two vector registers together results in the addition of the pairs of corresponding operands in the registers.

On the Cray-1, then, consider the execution of the following Fortran statements:

```
      R = S + T
      DO 2010 I = 1,64
         A(I) = B(I) + C(I)
 2010 CONTINUE
```

The first statement causes the scalar values S and T to be fetched from memory to S registers where they are added together with the result going to another S register that is subsequently stored into the address of R.

It is possible to execute loop 2010 with such scalar instructions as well, fetching and computing one pair of elements at a time. But with vector instructions, *all* of the elements of B can be fetched to a vector register, all of

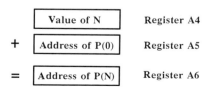

FIGURE 2.1
Address Register Calculation

C to another vector register, a single vector add instruction can be used to compute all of the sums, and a vector store instruction returns the results to the array A (Figure 2.2).

Instruction Stack

An instruction stack is a set of high speed registers that hold a copy of a small number of program instructions prefetched from memory by the computer system, acting as a small window moving over the executable program code. Instructions typically can issue from the instruction stack to the CPU at the rate of one instruction per clock cycle. If the next instruction to be issued is not on the instruction stack, the system must fetch it from memory. This memory fetch takes tens of clock cycles to complete. If every instruction had to be fetched from memory, a program might run an order of magnitude more slowly.

Each computer system has a different-sized instruction stack and different schemes for prefetching instructions to the stack. Occasionally, a critical feature of program optimization will be to make sure that a CPU-intensive DO loop or subprogram is entirely contained on the instruction stack during its execution.

2.1.3   Functional Units

Originally, the CPU of a computer was monolithic, executing one instruction to completion before beginning the next. This is still the cheapest way to build a CPU, but it completely denies the overlapped execution of independent instructions within a program. The CDC 6600 was one of the first computers to partition the CPU into its functional units, thus allowing address calculations and program arithmetic to proceed simultaneously. Con-

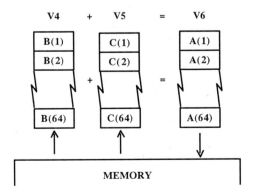

FIGURE 2.2.
Vector Addition

sider the following code excerpt:

```
X = Y * Z / (P + Q)
```

Assume that the values of Y and Z have been fetched to registers. Then when the multiply instruction has been issued, the fetch instructions for the values of P and Q can be issued. When the data arrives from memory, the add instruction can be issued as well. This is because each of the major functions of the CPU has been realized in a wholly independent unit of hardware. Compilers take advantage of multiple functional units by attempting to schedule as many independent operations as possible to achieve maximum overlap of instruction execution.

Note that whereas a computer might have hundreds of instructions, it will typically have about ten functional units, each one of which executes a family of related instructions. For example, a floating-point add functional unit performs both addition and subtraction, rounded or unrounded, normalized or unnormalized.

The CDC 6600 and 7600 each provided functional units for address computation, integer and floating-point scalar arithmetic, and logical operations. The Cray-1 contains a set of functional units very similar to its predecessors and a few additional units exclusively dedicated to vector processing.

Segmented Functional Units

A computer might be able to issue a new instruction in each clock cycle, but there are very few instructions that complete execution in just one clock cycle. For example, a floating-point add instruction might take four clock cycles to complete; a multiply or a divide might take even longer. For this reason, each functional unit is itself further partitioned into a number of independent segments, preferably one segment for each clock cycle of execution. By this means, a computer may issue several identical instructions in sequence as long as the operands are independent. Consider the execution of the following Fortran statements:

```
Z1 = X1 + Y1

Z2 = X2 + Y2

Z3 = X3 + Y3

Z4 = X4 + Y4
```

Assuming that the operands have already been fetched to registers, then the steps through time shown in Figure 2.3 indicate the operation of the segmented floating-point add unit.

The adder depicted in Figure 2.3 performs as an assembly line with four stations. As programmers we do not know what happens at each station, only that a completed sum flows off the end of the line. The segmentation of

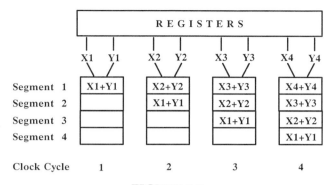

FIGURE 2.3.
Segmented Functional-Unit Operation

the adder generates one result per clock cycle instead of one result every four clock cycles achievable without segmentation (Figure 2.3).

The performance of a segmented functional unit is characterized by two features:

- Startup Time. This is the number of clock cycles prior to the generation of the first result. When segments are each one clock cycle long, the startup time is the number of segments. But this is not always the case — the divide unit on the CDC 7600 had two segments and a startup time of 27 clock cycles.

- Result Rate. This is directly related to the longest segment in a functional unit. In most units the segments are one clock cycle long, occasionally two, and in the 7600 divide unit, the first segment was 25 clock cycles long. After the startup time, a functional unit can deliver one result each time the longest segment completes its task.

Considering that most functional units can produce one result per clock cycle, and that several can run in parallel, a tremendous burden is placed on memory access to fetch operands and store results. One way to alleviate this burden is the use of memory banks.

2.1.4 Memory Banks

Each register of a computer is capable of delivering its contents to the CPU each clock cycle. But the registers are so expensive that it is not feasible to have more than a few hundred of them. The physical memory of a super-computer is typically millions or even billions of bytes and is necessarily much less expensive than the registers. One way to reduce cost is to build a memory unit that holds many memory locations and can service a request from the CPU to fetch from or store into any of those locations. For several reasons, all related to cost, such a unit will take several clock cycles to service a request and will queue all other requests in the interim. But the CPU can process data so fast that we must have a memory system that can deliver or receive data at a rate of at least one item per clock cycle.

One answer to the problem is to build a memory system from many units or "banks" and to arrange memory locations so that consecutive locations are assigned to the banks in a round-robin manner. The rate at which a bank can service requests is called the "bank cycle time," and so an effective memory system must have at least as many banks as the number of clock cycles in the bank cycle time. Since, typically, the most memory-intensive parts of a program involve the referencing of contiguous arrays in DO loops, this mapping of memory locations onto banks guarantees that each subsequent memory reference will be serviced by a different bank.

Bank cycle times on supercomputers are typically four or eight clock cycles, so a memory system of eight banks can be built with the following mapping of memory locations:

Memory Location	Bank Number
0	1
1	2
2	3
3	4
4	5
5	6
6	7
7	8
8	1
9	2
10	3
11	4
12	5
13	6
14	7
15	8
16	1
17	2
18	3
19	4
etc.	

Another way of looking at this is to picture the banks with memory locations spread across them as shown in Figure 2.4.

Given the Fortran declaration

DIMENSION A(512)

BANK

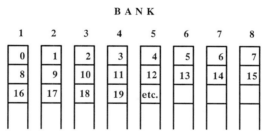

FIGURE 2.4.
Memory-Bank Allocation

then the elements of the array will be assigned to consecutive memory locations, which is to say, consecutive banks. Thus, when the array is referenced in a DO loop such as:

```
DO 2020 I = 1,8
    A(I) = A(I) + 1.0
2020 CONTINUE
```

then the fetch instructions for each successive element of the array A can be issued by the CPU and serviced by the memory system at the rate of one per clock cycle. Note that with eight memory banks, the successive requests for data in a given bank occur eight clock cycles apart (Figure 2.5).

When the memory-bank concept is coupled with a segmented-memory functional unit (seven segments), then Table 2.1 represents the flow of the array elements from memory to the CPU. It should be clear that this is a very effective use of the memory system and provides a nice balance between delivery of data from memory and the ability of the CPU to process it.

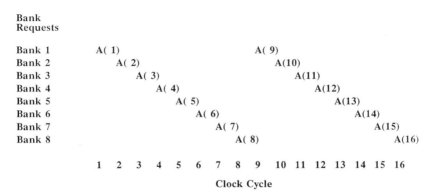

FIGURE 2.5.
Timing of Contiguous Bank Requests

TABLE 2.1 Timing of a Memory-to-Register Request

Clock Cycle	Instruction	Segmented Memory Unit							In Register
		1	2	3	4	5	6	7	
1	FETCH A(1)	A(1)	—	—	—	—	—	—	—
2	FETCH A(2)	A(2)	A(1)	—	—	—	—	—	—
3	FETCH A(3)	A(3)	A(2)	A(1)	—	—	—	—	—
4	FETCH A(4)	A(4)	A(3)	A(2)	A(1)	—	—	—	—
5	FETCH A(5)	A(5)	A(4)	A(3)	A(2)	A(1)	—	—	—
6	FETCH A(6)	A(6)	A(5)	A(4)	A(3)	A(2)	A(1)	—	—
7	FETCH A(7)	A(7)	A(6)	A(5)	A(4)	A(3)	A(2)	A(1)	—
8	FETCH A(8)	A(8)	A(7)	A(6)	A(5)	A(4)	A(3)	A(2)	A(1)
9	—	—	A(8)	A(7)	A(6)	A(5)	A(4)	A(3)	A(2)
10	—	—	—	A(8)	A(7)	A(6)	A(5)	A(4)	A(3)
11	—	—	—	—	A(8)	A(7)	A(6)	A(5)	A(4)
12	—	—	—	—	—	A(8)	A(7)	A(6)	A(5)
13	—	—	—	—	—	—	A(8)	A(7)	A(6)
14	—	—	—	—	—	—	—	A(8)	A(7)
15	—	—	—	—	—	—	—	—	A(8)

The following DO loop demonstrates a very ineffective use of the memory system.

```
      DO 2030 I = 1, 57, 8
         A(I) = A(I) + 1.0
2030 CONTINUE
```

Table 2.2 is the timing chart for these accesses.

Notice that the memory functional unit can accept an operand each CPU clock cycle. But the one memory bank in which all the requested elements reside can only supply an operand from its locations each memory bank cycle time, which as shown is four clock cycles. Therefore the effective transfer rate from memory to the CPU is reduced by a factor of four. Striding through memory as we did in loop 2030 results in "memory-bank conflicts," because the stride is such that the operands required are located in only one of the memory banks. Memory-bank conflicts will occur in references that have a stride through memory that is an integer multiple of

$$2 \times \frac{\text{number of memory banks}}{\text{bank cycle time (in clock cycles)}}$$

TABLE 2.2   Timing of a Strided Memory Request

Clock Cycle	Instruction	Segmented Memory Unit							In Register
		1	2	3	4	5	6	7	
1	FETCH A(1)	A(1)	—	—	—	—	—	—	—
2	FETCH A(9)	—	A(1)	—	—	—	—	—	—
3	FETCH A(17)	—	—	A(1)	—	—	—	—	—
4	FETCH A(25)	—	—	—	A(1)	—	—	—	—
5	FETCH A(33)	A(9)	—	—	—	A(1)	—	—	—
6	FETCH A(41)	—	A(9)	—	—	—	A(1)	—	—
7	FETCH A(49)	—	—	A(9)	—	—	—	A(1)	—
8	FETCH A(57)	—	—	—	A(9)	—	—	—	A(1)
9	—	A(17)	—	—	—	A(9)	—	—	—
10	—	—	A(17)	—	—	—	A(9)	—	—
11	—	—	—	A(17)	—	—	—	A(9)	—
12	—	—	—	—	A(17)	—	—	—	A(9)
13	—	A(25)	—	—	—	A(17)	—	—	—
14	—	—	A(25)	—	—	—	A(17)	—	—
15	—	—	—	A(25)	—	—	—	A(17)	—
16	—	—	—	—	A(25)	—	—	—	A(17)
					·				
					·				
					·				
25	—	A(49)	—	—	—	A(41)	—	—	—
26	—	—	A(49)	—	—	—	A(41)	—	—
27	—	—	—	A(49)	—	—	—	A(41)	—
28	—	—	—	—	A(49)	—	—	—	A(41)
29	—	A(57)	—	—	—	A(49)	—	—	—
30	—	—	A(57)	—	—	—	A(49)	—	—
31	—	—	—	A(57)	—	—	—	A(49)	—
32	—	—	—	—	A(57)	—	—	—	A(49)
33	—	—	—	—	—	A(57)	—	—	—
34	—	—	—	—	—	—	A(57)	—	—
35	—	—	—	—	—	—	—	A(57)	—
36	—	—	—	—	—	—	—	—	A(57)

In other words, bank conflicts will occur any time a stride causes successive references to a memory bank to occur in less than the bank cycle time. On a Cray-1 with eight memory banks, this can only happen if the stride is an integer multiple of $2 \times 8/4 = 4$.

It should be noted that the preceding formula works only for computers whose number of banks and bank cycle time (in clock cycles) are both powers of two, characteristics shared by most current supercomputers that utilize memory banks.

2.1.5   Memory Caches

A memory cache is a small, fast, expensive memory placed between the very fast CPU registers and the large slow main memory of a machine. When the

CPU requests a data item from memory, the hardware checks to see if the item is resident in the cache, and, if so, it delivers it to the CPU, typically in two clock cycles. If the item is not in the cache, the hardware requests a packet of data from main memory to the cache that includes the item requested plus (usually) three more items as well, on the assumption that the data will be referenced contiguously. Assuming that the transfer from memory to cache takes 12 clock cycles, then the time to transfer one item from memory to CPU is:

Transfer four items to cache	12 clock cycles
Transfer one item to CPU	2 " "
Total	14 clock cycles

and if the other three items are subsequently referenced from the cache, then the total cost in time to transfer data to the CPU is:

Transfer of second item to CPU	12 clock cycles
Transfer of first item to CPU	2 " "
Transfer of second item to CPU	2 " "
Transfer of third item to CPU	2 " "
Transfer of fourth item to CPU	2 " "
Total	20 clock cycles

or   5 clock cycles per item transferred

All subsequent references to the data items will be satisfied in two clock cycles, as long as they remain in the cache. (Since the cache is smaller than the main memory, requests for other data might overwrite previously requested data.)

Most cache systems also use the cache for instructions as well as data operands.

2.1.6   Instruction Streams and Data Streams

Computers may be categorized according to whether they have one or many instruction streams and one or many data streams.* Of four possible categories, one defines the simplest conventional computers, one is never implemented, and the two remaining contain all supercomputers.

Single Instruction Stream, Single Data Stream (SISD)

The SISD category of course describes the relatively simple computers that perform each instruction of a program to completion before beginning the next instruction. There is no possibility of overlap within the machine, and therefore only one stream of data through the CPU.

---

* Michael J. Flynn, "Very High-Speed Computing Systems", *Proceedings of the IEEE* 54 (1966).

Single Instruction Stream, Multiple Data Stream (SIMD)

This category defines a computer system having a single instruction processor and multiple arithmetic and logical processors, thereby allowing simultaneous computation to be performed on different streams of data. There are two very important subcategories within SIMD: 1) the single CPU partitioned into independent functional units, each performing different operations on specific data streams; and 2) multiple identical arithmetic logical units (ALUs), each being assigned the same instructions by the instruction processor but operating on different partitions of the program data.

The Partitioned CPU. We have seen in the preceding basic features that a single CPU designed as a collection of independent functional units can sustain several arithmetic and logical operations simultaneously. It is important to note that such a CPU contains only one instruction processor and so processes a single instruction stream, issuing the instructions one at a time. It is the functional units operating independently that allow new instructions to be issued before previous instructions have completed execution.

Examples of machines in this category are the single-processor Cray computers; the CYBER 205; the Fujitsu, Hitachi, and NEC supercomputers; the Alliant FX/1; the Convex C-1; and the SCS-40.

Multiple ALUs. Again, a single processor handles the stream of program instructions, and, in this subcategory, passes all instructions to a number of separate ALUs, each of which then operates on a different segment of the program data. Perhaps the example easiest to understand is the assignment of DO loop iterations to individual ALUs. Consider:

```
      DO 2040 I = 1, N
         A(I) = B(I) + C(I)
 2040 CONTINUE
```

In this case the instruction processor will assign to each ALU the task of adding C(I) to B(I) and storing the result in A(I) *but* will pass a different value of I to each. If there are fewer ALUs than loop iterations, the instruction processor will continue to issue the instructions until all values of I have been processed. If there are more ALUs than loop iterations, the extra ALUs will be "turned off" during execution of the loop instructions.

Turning off an ALU can mean different things on different systems. It might mean that the ALU receives instructions and ignores them or it might perform the computation but not store any results. In any case, it is possible on any system to render an ALU ineffective at any point in the computation.

Now consider how the multiple-ALU SIMD machines handle conditional code:

```
DO 2050 I = 1, N
    IF ( D(I) .GT. EPSLON) THEN
        A(I) = B(I) + C(I)
    ENDIF
    B(I) = D(I) * 2.0
2050 CONTINUE
```

Since all ALUs must receive the same instructions, the instruction processor issues the following commands to each:

- For your value of I, compute D(I) .GT. EPSLON, and, if false, turn yourself off.

- For your value of I, compute B(I) + C(I), and store into A(I). The "off" ALUs will receive this instruction but not act on it.

- Turn yourself on. (Redundant and meaningless to the "on" ALUs but well-received by those previously turned "off.")

- For your value of I, compute D(I) * 2.0, and store into B(I).

Things become more complicated if the loop has an indefinite termination:

```
DO 2060 I = 1, N
    IF (A(I) .LT. 0.) GO TO 2061
        A(I) = A(I) - B(I)
2060 CONTINUE
     . . .
2061 CONTINUE
```

Let "iend" be the first value of I such that A(iend).LT.O. Here no values are to be stored into the array A for I.GE.iend, but if the same mechanism were employed as we did with loop 2050, A(I) would be modified for any value of I for which A(I).GE.O., whether or not I.LT.iend. Some multiple-ALU SIMD machines have only cumbersome mechanisms for reporting the state of one ALU either to the instruction processor or to the other ALUs, so many systems resort to running such loops on a single ALU, one iteration at a time.

Examples of machines in this category are the ILLIAC IV, Burroughs BSP, SAXPY Matrix-1, and Thinking Machines' Connection Machine.

Multiple Instruction Stream, Single Data Stream (MISD)

Now don't get misty over this, but there are no computers that issue multiple instructions against a single stream of data.

Multiple Instruction Stream, Multiple Data Stream (MIMD)

As the name implies, these machines have multiple instruction processors as well as a means to overlap execution of instructions. Some are simply multiple CPUs sharing a common memory, and their simplest (and most common) use is to assign entirely separate programs residing in disjoint parts of the memory to each CPU. This is just a minor step up from the multiprogramming already common on single CPU systems, where several programs reside in the computer's memory and the CPU is assigned to each in turn.

A more exciting and more complicated application of such systems is to assign several CPUs to execute the instructions of a single program. Here it is again necessary to cause each CPU to work on different segments of the program data, but unlike the multiple-ALU SIMD machines — which work in lock step, each either performing or ignoring the same instruction seen by the other ALUs — the MIMD CPUs each perform a unique version of the instruction stream independent of the others. At critical points in the program, the CPUs must be forced to synchronize with one another, either to properly pass information among themselves or to correctly share a common memory location. Consider the following conditional dot-product calculation:

```
DO 2070 I = 1,1000
    IF (B(I) .GT. EPSLON) THEN
        SDOT = SDOT + B(I) * C(I)
    ENDIF
2070 CONTINUE
```

Ignoring numerical considerations as to the order in which computation is performed, we could imagine that each of four processors could be assigned to compute the dot product in the index ranges 1–250, 251–500, 501–750, and 751–1000. But notice that each processor would be asynchronously updating the variable SDOT. Conceptually, two processors could fetch the same value of SDOT, add their terms to it, and store it back. The first value stored would be overwritten by the second, and some terms in the sum would be lost.

Examples of machines in this category are the multiprocessor Cray X-MPs, Alliant Fx/8, the BBN Butterfly, and the various hypercubes.

2.1.7 Summary

In Chapter 1 we stated that the following loop required at least 400 scalar instructions to perform the desired addition:

```
DO 1020 I = 1, 100
    ARRAY1(I) = ARRAY2(I) + ARRAY3(I)
1020 CONTINUE
```

In fact, considering the incrementation of the index and the test and branch instruction necessary for the loop, a minimum of six instructions per iteration is needed to complete the computation. Now assume a scalar computer with enough resources (registers, paths into memory, etc.) such that the execution of each instruction can be overlapped with all others. Then, given that the computer can issue one instruction per clock cycle, we see that a peak performance of one result every six clock cycles can be achieved.

Even though the floating-point add functional unit can receive new operands and deliver results at the rate of one per clock cycle, the instruction issue rate causes the add instructions to be issued only every six clock cycles. It should be clear, then, that as long as each operation requires the issue of a machine instruction, further parallelism in a single scalar CPU will have no payoff. It was this realization that led to the development in the 1970s of the "vector" processor.

2.2
THE VECTOR PROCESSOR

Of all the supercomputer designs, the single-CPU vector processor is certainly the most successful to date, and the one that has received the most attention from Fortran compiler writers. We therefore will direct our attention to the details of several such designs.

There are two major categories of vector processors; memory-to-memory machines and register-to-register machines. Each has its own advantages and disadvantages in the handling of typical Fortran code.

2.2.1 Memory-to-Memory Vector Processors

CDC's Star 100 was one of the first available vector processors, and it has since evolved through the CYBER 203 to the CYBER 205. Its general architecture is the heart of the newly announced ETA 10. In scalar mode, these computers utilize a set of 256 general-purpose registers to hold operands and results during computation. But in vector mode these CDC machines fetch vector operands directly from memory to the CPU and store vector results directly back into memory, with no intervening registers. Since almost all the computers in this class are CYBER 205s we will limit our discussion to this machine, with occasional reference to improvements announced in the design of the ETA 10.

CYBER 205 Characteristics

The CYBER 205 is a virtual memory system. It has a large physical memory of up to eight million 64-bit words, and a virtual address space of over two trillion 64-bit words. The hardware is capable of addressing bits, bytes, half-words (32 bits), full words (64 bits), superwords (or "swords," which are eight contiguous full words), and double swords. Each one million words of memory is arranged in 16 "stacks" of eight banks each. Data items are stored in half-words across the stacks, so one sword of data is represented by 16 half-words, one from each of the stacks. The memory bank cycle time is four clock cycles. The machine has a clock cycle of 20 nanoseconds and in vector mode can fetch two swords and store one sword simultaneously, at a combined rate of three words per clock cycle.

The arithmetic, logical, and memory operations of the CPU are carried out by two sets of segmented functional units, one exclusively for scalar instructions, the other for vector floating point. There are functional units for scalar integer arithmetic, logical operations, and scalar floating-point add/subtract, multiply, divide, and square root. The vector functional units perform floating-point add/subtract, multiply, divide, and square root.

Basic Vector Operations. CYBER 205 vector operations are performed in either one, two, or four pipelines, depending on the model of the machine. Each pipeline can perform one 64-bit or two 32-bit floating-point results

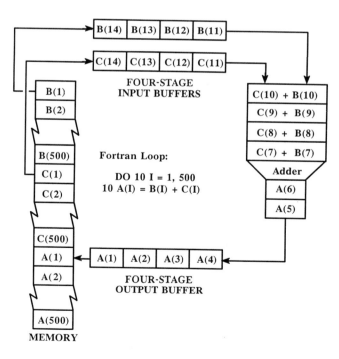

FIGURE 2.6.
CYBER 205 Memory-to-Memory Vector Pipeline.

each clock cycle. So on a four-pipeline machine, as many as eight results per clock cycle can flow out of the pipeline and back to memory. Figure 2.6 illustrates the flow of data from memory through one pipeline and back to memory again in a simple 64-bit floating-point vector instruction on the CYBER 205.

The result rate of one per clock cycle matches the performance of computers that use high-speed registers for operands and results. This is achieved by a special memory interface that fetches and stores data in superwords (eight contiguous 64-bit words). After a startup time, a rate of two 64-bit words fetched and one 64-bit word stored per clock cycle per pipeline can be maintained. Keep in mind that if, for any reason, not all operands are used, or not all results are stored, the memory interface still must fetch and store the data in swords, and the effective data rate goes down accordingly.

The input and output buffers aid in the resolution of memory bank conflicts among the input operands and the ouput results.

As shown, the single pipeline is generating one 64-bit floating-point add result per clock cycle. In 32-bit floating-point mode, each pipeline is capable of generating two results per clock cycle. Focusing on just the add unit, this can be depicted as in Figure 2.7. Here, each 64-bit section of the arrays B and C is split upon arrival into two 32-bit input operands, the effect being a result rate of two per clock cycle — double that of 64-bit arithmetic.

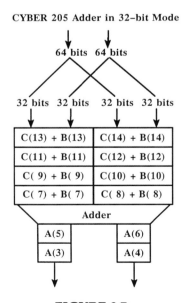

FIGURE 2.7.
CYBER 205 Vector Add Functional Unit in 32-Bit Mode

Now consider that a fully configured CYBER 205 has four such pipelines, so the total result rate can be four 64-bit or eight 32-bit floating-point results per clock cycle.

Linked Triad.   Under many circumstances, the add and multiply pipelines can be linked together, one producing a result fed directly into the other — thus again doubling the result rate. A DO loop that could utilize this "linked-triad" capability is

```
      DO 2080 I = 1, 10000
         A(I) = SCA * B(I) + C(I)
 2080 CONTINUE
```

Figure 2.8 is a diagram of the linked functional units in a single 64-bit pipeline. The linked-triad instruction performing 32-bit operations on a four-pipeline machine generates 16 floating point results per clock cycle or about 800 million floating-point operations per second.

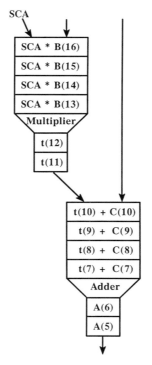

FIGURE 2.8.
CYBER 205 Linked-Triad Operation. "t" represents the
intermediate results flowing from the multiplier to the adder.

Gather/Scatter Periodic. The vector pipeline instructions of the CYBER 205 always operate on *contiguous* data; data references with a stride other than +1 require special treatment. An additional device, the "stream unit," performs many special-purpose data-motion operations, among which are the "gather-periodic" and "scatter-periodic" instructions, which specifically handle strided data. These instructions can be used to vectorize the following loop:

```
      DO 2090 I = 1, 10000, 10
         A(I) = B(I) + C(I)
 2090 CONTINUE
```

Here the vector pipeline cannot directly fetch or store every tenth item of data. So the vector stream unit issues gather-periodic instructions to fetch the necessary data from the B and C arrays and stores the data into temporary contiguous arrays in memory. Then these temporary arrays are added in the vector pipeline with another temporary array created to hold contiguous results. Finally, the stream unit issues a scatter-periodic instruction to fetch the contiguous result array and place the answers into every tenth element of the array A. It is as if the following loops were executed:

```
Comment: Periodically gather every tenth element of B
         K = 0
         DO 2091 I = 1, 10000, 10
            K = K + 1
            TEMPB(K) = B(I)
    2091 CONTINUE

Comment: Periodically gather every tenth element of C
         K = 0
         DO 2092 I = 1, 10000, 10
            K = K + 1
            TEMPC(K) = C(I)
    2092 CONTINUE

Comment: Perform vector addition of gathered arrays
         DO 2093 J = 1, K
            TEMPA(J) = TEMPB(J) + TEMPC(J)
    2093 CONTINUE

Comment: Periodically scatter results into every tenth element of A
         K = 0
         DO 2094 I = 1, 10000, 10
            K = K + 1
            A(I) = TEMPA(K)
    2094 CONTINUE
```

Gather/Scatter Random. With the related instructions "gather random" and "scatter random," the stream unit also handles indirect addressing. So in the following loop the stream unit "gathers" temporary contiguous vectors by applying the values in the array IB to the array B and the values of IC to C.

The add of the temporary vectors is then performed in the vector pipeline, with the results going to another temporary array. Finally, the stream unit then "scatters" the temporary array of results into the array A under control of the index array IA.

```
      DO 2100 I = 1, 10000
          A(IA(I)) = B(IB(I)) + C(IC(I))
2100 CONTINUE
```

In handling the preceding loop, essentially the following operations are performed:

```
Comment: Randomly gather the indirectly addressed elements of B
         DO 2101 I = 1, 10000
             TEMPB(I) = B(IB(I))
    2101 CONTINUE

Comment: Randomly gather the indirectly addressed elements of C
         DO 2102 I = 1, 10000
             TEMPC(I) = C(IC(I))
    2102 CONTINUE

Comment: Perform vector addition of gathered arrays
         DO 2103 I = 1, 10000
             TEMPA(I) = TEMPB(I) + TEMPC(I)
    2103 CONTINUE

Comment: Randomly scatter results into every tenth element of A
         DO 2104 I = 1, 10000
             A(IA(I)) = TEMPA(I)
    2104 CONTINUE
```

Bit Vectors.   The stream unit also generates and manipulates bit vectors. A bit vector is a field in memory of up to 65,535 bits, each of which can be set or interrogated. One of the common uses of a bit vector is as a mask in a conditional operation. A bit vector could be used to control the operations in the following DO loop:

```
      DO 2110 I = 1, 10000
          IF ( B(I) .GT. EPSLON) THEN
              A(I) = B(I)**2 + C(I) / SCA
              D(I) = SQRT (A(I)) * C(I)
          ENDIF
2110 CONTINUE
```

A bit vector of length 10,000 can be generated by setting the Ith bit to one or zero, depending on whether the relational expression "B(I) .GT. EPSLON" is true or false, respectively. All computation within the IF-block can then be performed with special instructions that perform the desired operations over the entire range 1 to 10000, skipping the computation of any elements associated with a bit whose value is zero.

An alternate way to perform loop 2110 on a CYBER 205 would be to utilize the bit vector to perform compress/decompress operations. In this case, special vector pipeline instructions gather up the elements of interest [i.e., where the condition B(I) .GT. EPSLON is true] into temporary arrays in memory, the arithmetic is performed with simple vector operations on the temporary arrays, then the answers are decompressed back into the arrays A and D. In essence the following operations are performed:

```
Comment: Compress elements of B and C into TEMPB and TEMPC
         K = 0
         DO 2111 I = 1, 10000
            IF ( B(I) .GT. EPSLON) THEN
               K = K + 1
               TEMPB(K) = B(I)
               TEMPC(K) = C(I)
            ENDIF
   2111 CONTINUE

Comment: Perform vector arithmetic on compressed vectors
         DO 2112 I = 1,K
            TEMPA(I) = TEMPB(I)**2 + TEMPC(I) / SCA
            TEMPD(I) = SQRT (TEMPA(I)) * TEMPC(I)
   2112 CONTINUE

Comment: Decompress results into arrays A and D
         K = 0
         DO 2113 I = 1, 10000
            IF ( B(I) .GT. EPSLON) THEN
               K = K + 1
               A(I) = TEMPA(K)
               D(I) = TEMPD(K)
            ENDIF
   2113 CONTINUE
```

Finally, the stream unit performs many high-level vector instructions typically realized in hardware on other computer systems. These include dot product, sum of elements, product of elements, first difference, average, vector reverse, and many more.

We have stated in this chapter that the important characteristics of functional units are their startup time and result rate. Table 2.3 lists the values for some common instructions used by Fortran programs. These are tabulated both for two-pipeline and four-pipeline CYBER 205s and for 32-bit and 64-bit arithmetic.

Vector length of an instruction can be up to 65,535 on the CYBER 205, so from Table 2.3 it should be clear that for very long vectors the startup time is of little importance. For example, in 64-bit mode on a two-pipeline machine, the addition of two 10,000-element vectors requires 5051 clock cycles, or 0.51 cycles per element. Conversely, short vector processing is completely dominated by the startup time of each instruction. The sum of two ten-element vectors on the same configuration takes 56 clock cycles, or 5.6 cycles per element. Multiple pipelines actually exacerbate this problem by further

TABLE 2.3   Selected Vector Operation Times, CYBER 205[a]

Operation	Time, 64 Bit		Time, 32 Bit	
	2-Pipe	4-Pipe	2-Pipe	4-Pipe
Add/Subtract	$51 + N/2$	$51 + N/4$	$51 + N/4$	$51 + N/8$
Multiply	$52 + N/2$	$52 + N/4$	$52 + N/4$	$52 + N/8$
Linked Vector Add and Mult Triad	$103 + N/2$	$103 + N/4$	$103 + N/4$	$103 + N/8$
Divide	$80 + N/.28$	$80 + N/.56$	$68 + N/.5$	$68 + N$
Square Root	$79 + N/.28$	$79 + N/.56$	$67 + N/.5$	$67 + N$
Scatter Vector A Randomly	$83 + N/.8$	$83 + N/.8$	$83 + N/.8$	$83 + N/.8$
Scatter Vector A Periodically	$71 + N/.8$	$71 + N/.8$	$71 + N/.8$	$71 + N/.8$
Gather Vector A Randomly	$69 + N/.8$	$69 + N/.8$	$69 + N/.8$	$69 + N/.8$
Gather Vector A Periodically	$39 + N/.8$	$39 + N/.8$	$39 + N/.8$	$39 + N/.8$
Compress Vector A (Z # of element compressed)	$52 + Z/2$	$52 + Z/4$	$52 + Z/4$	$52 + Z/8$
Expand Vector A (Z # of elements expanded)	$58 + Z/2$	$58 + Z/4$	$58 + Z/4$	$58 + Z/8$
Sum of Elements	$116 + N$	$116 + N$	$116 + N$	$116 + N$
Dot Product	$116 + N$	$116 + N$	$116 + N$	$116 + N$

[a] Vector length = N. Format is startup time + result rate. Table derived from Clifford N. Arnold, "Vector Optimization on the CYBER 205," Control Data Corporation, Arden Hills, MN.

shortening the vector seen by each pipeline, but the startup time remains constant. In other words on a four-pipeline machine adding two ten-element vectors requires 53.5 clock cycles, only a 4.5% improvement, rather than the 50% improvement we see on very long vectors. The crossover point between scalar and vector performance on the CYBER 205 is on the order of length 50 for most calculations.

Note that, in Table 2.3, operations carried out by the stream unit are insensitive either to the number of pipelines or the precision of the data.

2.2.2   ETA 10

The ETA 10 is a computer system composed of from one to eight CPUs similar in architecture to the CYBER 205. Each CPU has four million 64-bit words of memory and two vector pipelines, sharing a common memory of 256 million 64-bit words. The common memory acts as a page server to the CPUs. The system has been initially released with a 12.5-nsec clock cycle, eventually to be lowered to 7 nsec. More important, the vector startup times have been lowered by about a factor of four to five, making short vector performance much better than on the original CYBER 205.

2.2.3   Register-to-Register Vector Processors

These machines move data from memory to vector registers and perform computations with vector-register operands, placing results again into vector registers. These results are either retained for further use or stored back into memory. The first register-to-register vector processor was the Cray-1, and the same architecture has been used in the follow-on machines, the Cray-1S, the Cray X-MP and the Cray-2. In fact, all other vector processors except the CYBER 205 and ETA 10 are register-to-register machines, remarkably similar to the Cray computers in basic features. So we will concentrate on these as a basis for this discussion, with occasional reference to other computers that have some important additional features.

Basic Characteristics

The major characteristics affecting performance of Fortran programs on this class of machines are

- Clock cycle

- Instruction issue rate

- Size and number of vector registers

- Memory size

- Number of concurrent paths to memory

- Ability to fetch/store vectors with a stride

- Number of duplicate arithmetic functional units (multiple vector pipe-lines)

- Whether functional units can be "chained" together

- Indirect addressing capability

- Handling of conditional blocks of code

Clock Cycle.   Earlier in this chapter we stated that if all other features of a computer system remained the same, then performance would vary inversely with the clock cycle. But, across different computer systems, the clock speed is not always a good comparison. For example, the Alliant FX/8 has a clock cycle of 167 nsec, but the architecture of the system allows a fully optimized code to run as much as 32 times faster than pure scalar execution. And the FX/8 sometimes approaches (or even surpasses) the performance of a Cray-1 with a 12.5-nsec clock.

Instruction Issue Rate. We have said that computers typically can issue one instruction per clock cycle, but the peak rate at which the Cray-2 can issue instructions is one every two clock cycles. So, although the Cray-2 has a 4.1-nsec clock, its effective clock speed in scalar mode is 8.2 nsec. Viewed in the context of Amdahl's law, this can have a drastic effect on any program not highly vectorized.

Vector Registers. All Cray computers have eight vector registers, each having 64 elements that are 64 bits wide. When a loop of arbitrary length is "vectorized," it is done in vector strips of length 64. Consider the loop:

```
      DO 2120 I = 1, N
         A(I) = B(I) + C(I)
2120  CONTINUE
```

In effect, this is performed on a Cray in the following way:

```
      NMOD64 = MOD (N, 64)
      DO 2121 I = 1, NMOD64
         A(I) = B(I) + C(I)
2121  CONTINUE

      I = NMOD64
      DO 2122 J = NMOD64+1, N, 64
         DO 2122 KOUNT = 1, 64
            I = I + 1
            A(I) = B(I) + C(I)
2122  CONTINUE
```

If N is not evenly divisible by 64, loop 2121 does the "remainder," or else it is not executed (NMOD64 = 0). Loop 2122 then performs a series of loops, each of exactly 64 in length to complete the computation. This technique is called "stripmining" a loop.

Note that if N is less than 64, loop 2121 performs all of the computation, and loop 2122 is never executed. The reason for doing the remainder first rather than last is that typical loops will have a remainder, and some loops will be shorter than length 64.

The number of elements in a vector register obviously determines the length of a "strip." Vector registers on the Alliant FX processors each have 32 elements, the IBM 3090 Vector Facility has registers of 128 elements, the NEC SX2 has 256 elements per register, and on the Fujitsu VP Series they are dynamically configurable in lengths of 32, 64, 128, 256, 512, or 1024 elements.

Perhaps a more subtle point regarding vector-register length is the startup time to fetch data from main memory to a vector register. (This startup time can also be thought of as the number of segments in a "memory functional unit.") On the Cray-1 and Cray-1S, startup is seven clock cycles. On the X-MP it is seventeen clock cycles, and the Cray-2 in its initial release has a startup time of 57 clock cycles. Never mind that the clock cycles get progressively shorter on these machines. The fact is that the average number of cycles per data item transferred is 1.125 on the Cray-1 and rises to 1.89 on the Cray-2, a significant difference in overhead cost.

Memory Size.   The amount of main memory available on vector processors can affect wall-clock-time performance of Fortran programs, more so than the CPU time for executing any particular program. On a virtual memory system, if the current data does not reside within the working set of pages, then thrashing can reduce performance to the speed of the secondary storage — disks, usually. In the worst case, this can cause a program's performance to be limited by the speed of sound (rate at which disks spin), rather than the speed of light. On a physical memory machine, a very large program will force the programmer to adopt I/O techniques to move data between main and secondary storage, with much the same possible performance degradation that occurs on virtual systems.

It should be obvious, then, that the larger the main memory of a computer, the less often we will face these problems, regardless of any other limitations of a given machine. Currently, the largest available main memory is on the Cray-2, with 268,435,456 64-bit words — casually referred to as 256 million words (which is exact if we assume that a million is $2**20 = 1,048,576$). This is at least eight times larger than main memory on other supercomputers, although newer, larger models of every machine are developed each year. The difference between the casual and actual memory sizes of the Cray-2 is larger than the total main memory available on most computers.

Number of Memory Paths.   The number of independent paths into memory can greatly affect the capability of a machine to overlap instructions, especially in relatively simple loops involving several different arrays (i.e., a loop in which almost every arithmetic operation is matched with a memory fetch or store of a vector). The Cray-1, Cray-1S, and Cray-2 each have one path into main memory, and it provides both fetching and storing of data but not both at the same time. The Cray X-MP has two fetch paths and one store path, all of which can operate concurrently. Thus in the simple loop:

```
      DO 2130 I = 1, 64
         A(I) = B(I) + C(I)
 2130 CONTINUE
```

the Cray-1 performs the following steps:

- Fetches the vector B(1:64) to a vector register

- Fetches the vector C(1:64) to another vector register, adds it to the previously fetched B(1:64), and places the result in a third vector register

- Stores the final result into A(1:64)

The Cray X-MP, with its extra memory paths:

- Fetches the vector B(1:64) to a vector register, while simultaneously fetching C(1:64), and, as soon as B(1) and C(1) have arrived, begins adding the vectors together, placing the results in a third vector register while simultaneously storing the results into A(1:64). (What a mouthful!)

Here we have used the ANSI 8X Fortran "array section" notation to indicate ranges of elements in the arrays. This will be fully discussed in Chapter 3.

Figure 2.9 indicates the relative cost in clock cycles for the preceding loop on the Cray-1 and X-MP. Note that if the X-MP had only one memory path like the Cray-1, then the difference in performance would have only been the ratio of their respective clock cycles, $12.5/8.5 = 1.5$. But, strictly because of additional memory paths, the performance ratio is $2812/782 = 3.6!$

A fully configured Fujitsu vector processor has two memory paths that can either fetch or store vector operands. The Hitachi S820 has three memory paths devoted to fetching only, and one that can handle either fetching or

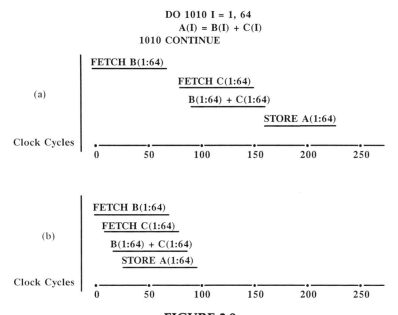

FIGURE 2.9.

Timing Diagram for Vector Addition. (a) Cray 1S, clock cycle = 12.5 nsec; 225 CC, 2812 nsec, 23 Mflops. (b) Cray X-MP, clock cycle = 8.5 nsec; 92 CC, 782 nsec, 84 Mflops.

storing. The NEC SX2 has two fetch paths and two store paths. All three of these machines have wider memory paths than does a Cray X-MP processor. For example, the maximum throughput on one memory path of the Cray X-MP is one word per clock cycle. The Fujitsu VP 400 can deliver four words per clock cycle on each memory path, and the fully configured Hitachi and NEC machines also have this capability.

These multiword memory paths split up the work of a single operation; they cannot be devoted independently to different operations. So, for example, adding vectors B and C and storing the result in vector A on the SX2 will result in one memory path devoted to delivering four elements of B per clock cycle, another delivering four elements of C, and still another delivering four elements per clock cycle into A.

Finally, even though we class these machines as register-to-register vector processors, some of them (not Cray) have instructions that can take one operand from a vector register and another directly from memory to the CPU. This added benefit allows such machines to utilize vector registers strictly for data that will be used more than once in the current loop being computed, a luxury that the Cray computers lack.

Fetch and Store Vectors with a Stride. All of the register-to-register vector processors regard a simple vector in memory to be represented by a starting address, a length, and a stride. Each has memory instructions that can fetch and store such data structures. From the point of view of the instruction set, each of the following loops is equally easy to execute in vector mode:

```
      DO 2140 I = 1, 100
         A(I) = B(I) + C(I)
 2140 CONTINUE

      DO 2150 I = 1, 1281, 128
         A(I) = B(I) + C(I)
 2150 CONTINUE

      DO 2160 I = 100000, 0, -1000
         A(I) = B(I) + C(I)
 2160 CONTINUE
```

However, the second loop, with its stride of 128, will certainly cause memory-bank conflicts on every supercomputer and consequently will run at least four or eight times more slowly than loop 2140 with its stride of one. The negative stride of loop 2160 will execute just as quickly as it would if the stride were positive.

Beyond memory-bank conflicts, some of the machines—such as the IBM 3090 Vector Facility, Alliant FX/8, and the Convex C-1—use cache memory between the main memory and the vector registers. We discussed earlier that it is the nature of cache to fetch more words than just the one requested, so strided data will not utilize the full memory transfer rate as can be done on systems without cache.

Finally, on virtual memory systems, a large stride can cause a great many page faults within the system, with relatively little use of the data moved to and from slow auxiliary storage.

Number of Vector Pipelines.   On the Cray computers there is only one of each kind of functional unit in a CPU: one adder, one multiplier, and so forth. The Convex C-1 and C-MP and the Japanese supercomputers made by Fujitsu, Hitachi, and NEC each has multiple copies of the vector functional units or multiple "pipelines." For these machines, the multiple pipelines act in a manner similar to those of the CYBER 205; that is, all duplicate functional units work on the same vectors, each taking a separate segment of the data. In effect, it is as if the vector length were divided by the number of pipelines, with the time to complete a vector operation reduced by about the same factor.

Chaining.   On all of the register-to-register vector processors except the Cray-2, the vector functional units can be "chained" together, thus allowing overlap of related operations. This is similar to the "linked triad" on the CYBER 205 but generally more flexible in that any combination of operations—not just the multiply and add functions—can be chained. But in practice, multiply—add combinations are by far the most common in Fortran programming. Consider the following loop as it is executed on a Cray X-MP:

```
      DO 2170 I = 1,64
         A(I) = 3.0 * A(I) + (2.0 + B(I)) * C(I)
 2170 CONTINUE
```

The values 3.0 and 2.0 will be set into scalar registers before the loop begins. Then the following steps will take place:

- Begin to fetch the vector of values A(1:64) to a vector register.

- Begin to fetch the vector of values B(1:64) to another vector register (overlapped in time with the previous fetch).

- As soon as B(1) arrives at its vector register, also pass it (and then all subsequent elements) to the adder, along with the scalar value 2.0. This "chains" the vector fetch to the add functional unit.

- As soon as A(1) arrives at its vector register, also pass it (and then all subsequent elements) to the multiplier, along with the scalar value 3.0 [this overlaps with the above computation 2.0 + B(1:64)].

- Issue the fetch instruction for C(1:64). This instruction will wait for a memory functional unit to complete one of the previous fetches, at which time the elements of C will begin to flow up from memory. [Note that this "wait" will also assure that the multiply functional unit will have completed 3.0 * A(1:64) by the time it is needed in the next step.]

- As soon as C(1) arrives at its vector register, also pass it (and then all subsequent elements) to the multiplier, along with the previously computed values of 2.0 + B(1:64). This chains the vector fetch to the multiply functional unit.

- As soon as (2.0 + B(1:64)) * C(1:64) exits the multiplier and enters its vector register, chain it to the add functional unit along with the previously computed vector register of 3.0 * A(1:64).

- As soon as the first result exits the add functional unit, chain it to the store functional unit to return the answers to memory.

A timing diagram of these steps is shown in Figure 2.10. Here we have eliminated the clock-cycle count in the abscissa to highlight the two distinct portions of the computation in which operations have been overlapped and chained together. These "chained vector times" or "chimes" are the dominant feature of the timing diagram. Ignoring the startup time of a vector instruction, a chime represents a number of clock cycles approximately equal to the vector length, in this case 64. It should be obvious that if a computer system can perform an operation in two chimes instead of four, there is a 50% savings in time.

A new chime must begin each time the system wants to reuse some resource, either a vector functional unit or an operand vector register. To illustrate this point, consider the chime diagrams for the Cray-1, which has only one memory functional unit, and the Cray-2 with one functional unit and overlapping but *no* chaining of vector instructions.

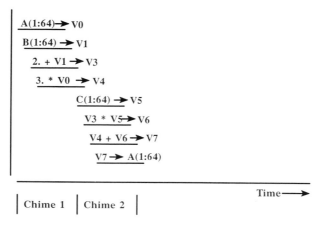

FIGURE 2.10.
Cray X-MP Chime Diagram

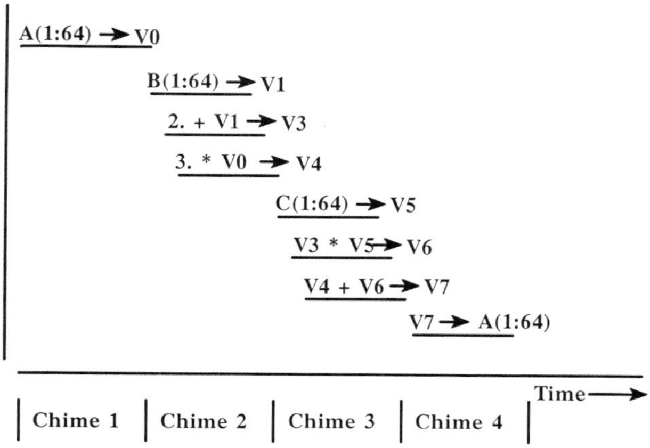

A(1:64) → V0

B(1:64) → V1

2. + V1 → V3

3. * V0 → V4

C(1:64) → V5

V3 * V5→ V6

V4 + V6 → V7

V7 → A(1:64)

Time →

| Chime 1 | Chime 2 | Chime 3 | Chime 4 |

FIGURE 2.11.
Cray-1 Chime Diagram

The clock cycles of the Cray-1, Cray X-MP, and Cray-2 are 12.5, 8.5, and 4.1 nsec, respectively. But because of differences in architecture they require four, two, and six chimes to complete the computation in the loop, so the absolute performance of each machine does not always reflect the differences in their clock speed. Given that a chime for this loop is roughly 64 clock cycles, then the approximate time for each machine is:

Cray-1:   4 chimes * 64 * 12.5 nsec = 3200 nsec
Cray X-MP: 2 chimes * 64 * 8.5 nsec = 1088 nsec
Cray-2:   6 chimes * 64 * 4.1 nsec = 1574 nsec

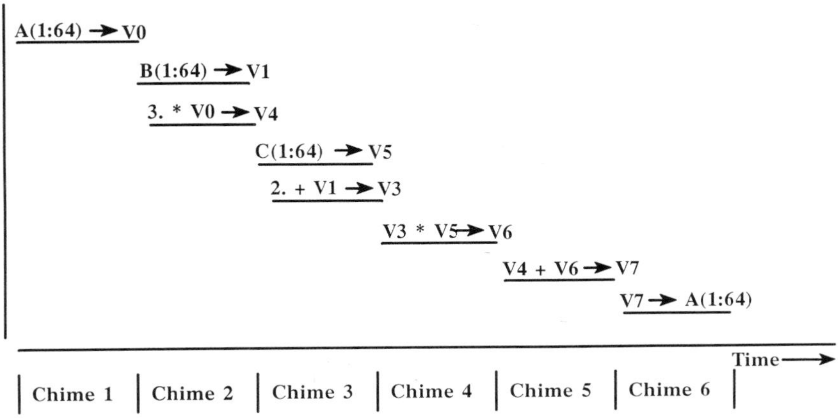

A(1:64) → V0

B(1:64) → V1

3. * V0 → V4

C(1:64) → V5

2. + V1 → V3

V3 * V5→ V6

V4 + V6 → V7

V7 → A(1:64)

Time →

| Chime 1 | Chime 2 | Chime 3 | Chime 4 | Chime 5 | Chime 6 |

FIGURE 2.12.
Cray-2 Chime Diagram

Remember, this is an analysis of just this particular loop. We shall see in chapter three that compilers have many ways to enhance performance in more complicated (more typical) loops.

The same kind of chime analysis can be done on all of the register-to-register vector processors and can be applied to almost any vectorizable loop. It is very valuable in predicting and understanding the performance of a supercomputer on any loop.

Indirect Addressing.   Consider the following indirect address loop:

```
      DO 2180 I = 1, 64
         A(IA(I)) = B(IB(I)) + C(IC(I))
 2180 CONTINUE
```

All the register-to-register vector processors except the Cray-1, Cray-1S, and the initial releases of the Cray X-MP and the SCS-40 have vector machine instructions to handle indirect addressing. These instructions could be utilized to perform loop 2180 in the following steps:

- Fetch the vector of values IB(1:64) to a vector register (V0).

- Fetch the vector of values IC(1:64) to another vector register (V1).

- Apply the values in V0 to the address of the array B, and fetch the values into another vector register (V2).

- Apply the values in V1 to the address of the array C, and fetch the values into another vector register (V3).

- Perform V2 + V3 = V4.

- Fetch the vector of values IA(1:64) to another vector register (V5).

- Store the values in register V4 into the array A indexed by the values in V5.

On machines with only one memory path, indirect addressing such as in loop 2180 will double the number of chimes required to perform the specified operations. Even on multiple memory-path machines, indirect addressing on one path will often disallow indirect addressing on another, thereby reducing overlapping and chaining of instructions. This is a hidden cost of indirect compared to direct addressing.

On those older machines that do not possess indirect address vector instructions, scalar instructions fetch the data, which are then accumulated into a vector register so that vector arithmetic instructions can be used. If this technique is not used with care, it can actually run more slowly than if pure scalar code had been used. A good rule of thumb on such machines is to run a loop in scalar mode if the number of indirect memory references exceeds the number of arithmetic operations.

Now consider a loop that has only one indirect index used to subscript all of the loop arrays, a fairly common occurrence in sparse matrix calculations:

```
        DO 2190 I = 1, 64
           A(JJ(I)) = B(JJ(I)) + C(JJ(I))
   2190 CONTINUE
```

Once the vector JJ(1:64) has been fetched to a vector register, it can be reused again and again to indirectly fetch and store the arrays of the computation; it need not be refetched for each of the other arrays as was the case with several different indirect indexes.

Finally, note that the ability to fetch and store data indirectly allows the vectorization of any array reference that appears in a loop (except where other circumstances prevent vectorization). In the following loop, each of the array indexes can be viewed as a vector of indirect address values to be computed at execution time:

```
        DO 2200 I = 1,N
           J = I * I / (I + 1)
           K = MOD (J, 10) + 1
           L = ISQRT (IA(I) * IB(I))
           M = 6 - M
           A(J) = (B(K) + C(L)) * D(M)
   2200 CONTINUE
```

Conditional Code Blocks.   All register-to-register vector processors have two means of handling conditional blocks of code; 1) the use of a vector-mask operation; and 2) the use of "compressed-index" instructions.* Knowing when the Fortran compiler will choose one of these techniques, and how to force it to use one or the other, are important points to learn for effective programming. The following loop illustrates both mechanisms:

```
        DO 2210 I = 1, N
           IF (X(I). GE. 0.0) Y(I) = A(I) + B(I)
   2210 CONTINUE
```

Each machine has a vector-mask register (VM) that has as many bits as there are elements in a vector register. For the Cray computers, the VM is 64 bits wide. The bits can be set to one or zero, depending on whether a vector condition is true or false. Remembering that the preceding loop will be stripmined into lengths matching the vector-register length, then for each strip the following steps can be taken on a Cray:

• Fetch the next 64 elements of X to a vector register (V0).

• Set the bits of VM to one where a corresponding element of V0 is positive, else set the bits to zero.

---

* Actually, Fujitsu vector processors have a third method, in which the operands of interest are compressed from one vector register to another.

- Fetch the next 64 elements of A to a vector register (V1).

- Fetch the next 64 elements of B to a vector register (V2).

- Compute V1 + V2 = V3 (for all elements).

- Fetch the next 64 elements of Y to a vector register (V4).

- Generate register V5 by choosing elements from V3 where the corresponding bit of VM is 1 and by choosing elements from V4 where the bits are zero.

- Store V5 into the 64 elements of the array Y.

Or to state it more simply, perform all the computation in vector mode for all elements, then store only those elements for which the condition is true.

These vector-mask operations are depicted in Figure 2.13 for X(I) .GE. 0.0 true for all odd values of I.

Although all computation of all elements is performed, vector-mask computation is so fast that it will outperform scalar mode any time that the condition is true a significant percentage of the time. Here, "significant percentage" depends highly on the number of operations being performed and could range from 5% to 100%.

On most non-Cray vector processors, the vector mask can control any operation—not just the final choice of elements—and this is very convenient in certain circumstances. In fact, for the simple operations of loop 2210, the add and store operations can be performed under control of the vector mask. This eliminates the need to fetch the vector Y or to build a vector register filled with old and new values for Y.

All the computer systems have simple mechanisms to determine if the VM is all zeroes or all ones, in order to skip any unnecessary steps.

There are two possible problems with using this vector-mask approach. First, if the condition is rarely true, the system must perform all the arithmetic for all elements, then store only a very few results. Even though vector mode is an order of magnitude faster than scalar mode, there is no payoff if the condition is true only 1% of the time. The more CPU intensive the computation is, the worse this problem becomes. Second, especially in the case of the Cray computers, the condition may be avoiding a singularity in the program. For example:

```
        DO 2220 I = 1, N
            IF (X(I). NE. 0.0) Y(I) = A(I) / X(I)
    2220 CONTINUE
```

It should be clear that if all elements of A are divided by all elements of X unconditionally, then any element with zero value will cause the program to abort. If compilers want to use vector-mask operations on loop 2220, they must have some guard against these singularities. On most of the non-Cray

Fetch X(1:64) to register V0

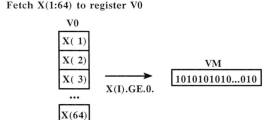

Fetch A(1:64) to V1 and B(1:64) to V2

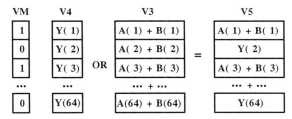

Fetch Y(1:64) to V4

VM	V4	V3		V5
1	Y(1)	A(1) + B(1)		A(1) + B(1)
0	Y(2)	A(2) + B(2)		Y(2)
1	Y(3) OR	A(3) + B(3)	=	A(3) + B(3)
...	...	... + ...		... + ...
0	Y(64)	A(64) + B(64)		Y(64)

Store V5 into Y

FIGURE 2.13.
Vector Mask Operations for Loop 2210

systems the vector-mask register can be applied to the divide operation so that only where the bit is one is the divide result actually generated. (It should be noted that this approach does not save any time: The divides associated with zero VM bits take just as long—they just do not generate singularities or deliver any results.)

In the "compressed-index" approach to the preceding DO loop, a vector register is generated containing those indexes where the condition is true. This register can then perform indirect address operations on the arrays involved. Computation is performed on only the elements that would be handled if the loop were executed in scalar mode. Here are the steps for loop 2220, using compressed-index instructions:

• Fetch the next 64 elements of X to a vector register (V0)

- Set the bits of VM to one, where a corresponding element of V0 is positive. Or set the bits to zero, *and* for each positive value of V0 set the next available element of register V7 to the corresponding index in the array X.

- Apply the values in V7 to the address of the array A, and fetch the values into another vector register (V1).

- Apply the values in V7 to the address of the array X, and fetch the values into another vector register (V2).

- Compute V1 / V2 = V3 (for all compressed elements).

- Store V3 into the array Y indexed by the values in V7.

To illustrate this compressed-index operation, assume that in loop 2220, X(I) is not equal to zero only for every thirtieth element. Then, for the first 64 elements, the register operations in Figure 2.14 depict the steps already outlined.

To summarize this section on conditional code, the following points should be kept in mind:

- Vector-mask operations are extremely fast and efficient for code executed under control of a condition that is usually true.

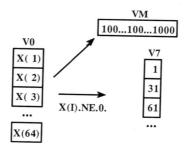

Fetch A and X indexed by V7 into V1 and V2

Store V3 into Y indexed by V7

FIGURE 2.14.
Compressed-Index Register Operations

- Since vector-mask operations perform all operations for all elements, chaining can take place.

- Vector-mask control performs calculations ultimately unused, so care is required to not introduce unacceptable overhead costs.

- On some systems, vector mask only applies to the final choice of answer, so singularities might occur, causing program abort.

- Compressed-index operations perform memory references with indirect addressing, inherently slower than direct memory references, and sometimes reducing chaining and overlapping of memory references with other operations within the loop.

- Compressed index will usually outperform vector mask for code executed under control of a condition that is true less than one-half the time.

- Compressed index operates on exactly the same elements as would be used in pure scalar mode, so no additional concern about singularities is introduced.

- All systems' vector processors have vector-mask operations, but some do not have compressed-index instructions. So for such machines, compressed index (done in software with scalar indirect addressing) will rarely outperform vector mask.

- In cases where conditional code is almost never executed, scalar mode might be faster than any vectorization technique.

Problems

1. Consider a memory-bank structure that has 256 banks, and the bank cycle time is 64 clock cycles. If the memory functional-unit time is $25 + N$, how long would it take, in clock cycles, to fetch 64 words from memory with strides of 1, 2, 4, 8, 16, 32, 64, 128, and 256?

2. The major bottleneck on a SISD machine is that only a single instruction can be issued each clock cycle. Explain how the following machines overcome this bottleneck and what category (SIMD or MIMD) each are:
   a. Uniprocessor of a Cray X-MP in vector mode.
   b. Multiprocessor of a Cray X-MP each operating in scalar mode.
   c. Multiprocessor of a Cray X-MP each operating in vector mode.
   d. Illiac IV.
   e. Alliant FX/8 using one processor in vector mode.
   f. Alliant FX/8 using eight processors in scalar mode.
   g. Alliant FX/8 using eight processors in vector mode.

3. On the CYBER 205, a vector operation under control of a bit vector is as

fast as the operation without bit vector control. Consider the following DO Loop:

```
INTEGER S
   ...
DO 10 I = 1, 10000, S
  A(I) = B(I) + C(I)
10    CONTINUE
```

The two methods of vectorizing this loop on the CYBER 205 are 1) periodically gather arrays B and C into temporary memory vectors TB and TC, add TB to TC, and store into temporary memory vector TA; then periodically scatter TA into A; or 2) add B to C over the entire index range 1 to 10000, using a bit vector that will only store into every 5th element of A.

Using the timings from Table 2.3, calculate the time needed for each method as a function of S. If $S = 1$, method 2 is faster; if $S = 500$, method 1 is faster. For what stride (S) does method 1 first become faster than method 2 for a 4-pipe CYBER 205 in 32-bit mode? For a 2-pipe CYBER 205 in 64-bit mode?

4. Vectorization of IF constructs on the CYBER 205 can be performed using bit vectors to control storage into the arrays. For example, for loop 2110 in the text, if we ignore the length of time taken to generate the bit vector for the condition B(I).GT.EPSLON, how often must the condition be true before the "controlled-store" approach runs faster than the compress/expand approach? (Use timings from Table 2.1.)

5. What is the minimum number of chimes required to perform each of the loops 41020 through 41039 in Appendix A on the Cray 1? On the Cray X-MP? On the Fujitsu VP200? What is the limiting resource within each CPU that results in this minimum number of chimes?

6. The optimal length for a vector register depends on the startup time for the vector operations. On the Cray-1, the CPU-time for the execution of:

```
DO 20 I = 1,N
  A(I) = B(I) + C(I)
20    CONTINUE
```

is approximately

$(INT((N-1)/64)+1) \times (25 + 3N) \times 12.5 \times 10^{-9}$ sec

  a. What is the Mflop rate for $N = 64$?
  b. What is the Mflop rate for $N = 128$?
  c. What would the Mflop rate be for $N = 64$ if the vector registers were 128 elements long?
  d. What would the Mflop rate be for $N = 128$ if the vector registers were 128 elements long?

e. Work problems a through d again for a time formula of:

$$(INT((N-1)/64)+1) \times (50 + 3N) \times 12.5 \times 10^{-9} \text{ sec}$$

7. On the Cray X-MP the second and third strip of 64 can overlap with the preceding strip. The Cray X-MP timing for loop 20 in the preceding exercise is approximately

$$(45+N) \times 8.5 \times 10^{-9} \text{ sec}$$

for $N \le 64$, and for $N > 64$ it is

$$(45 + N \bmod 64 + (INT((N-65)/64)+1)$$
$$\times (13+64)) \times 8.5 \times 10^{-9} \text{ sec}$$

For the Cray X-MP, answer problems a through d of the preceding exercise.

8. The text discusses two possible methods of vectorizing IF statements on a Cray X-MP. For loop 2210, assume that the conditional vector-merge approach runs in 3 chimes and the compressed-index approach runs in 5 chimes. What fraction of the elements of X must be ≥ 0.0 for the conditional vector-merge approach to run faster?

9. Why do some compilers refuse to vectorize loop 2000?

10. Things to try on your machine. Execute the following code on your machine. (You may have to reference a different timing function.)

```
      DO 100 K = 1, 128
      T1 = SECOND ( )
        DO 50 I = K, K*64, K
        A(I) = (B(I)*C(I))+(D(I)*E(I))
50      CONTINUE
      T2 = SECOND ( )
      PRINT *, K, T2-T1
100   CONTINUE
```

From the timing, can you determine how many memory banks your machine has?

3
FORTRAN

Fortran is the oldest of the high-level languages and possibly the most maligned. It is certain that new ideas enter new languages much faster than they can enter the old, and so it is relatively easy to criticize Fortran in comparison to more modern languages. But there are still many reasons to use Fortran and, consequently, to learn to use it well.

Corporations and universities have billions of dollars invested in existing and productive Fortran programs, and, as yet, no advocate of other languages has offered to translate from Fortran to their favorite at no cost. Even if free translation were available, the majority of scientists and engineers are well grounded in Fortran, and there would be considerable inertia to overcome to provide the same level of expertise and comfort with a new language. Even Fortran 8X, with its many new features and ideas, will be a daunting challenge to those who are comfortable with ANSI 77 Fortran.

Scientific computer vendors have made large investments in the development of optimizing Fortran compilers, almost to the exclusion of other languages — until recently. So even though the systems management part of a program might be better written in another language, when it comes to actually solving the equations of our application, we would be hard pressed to do it more efficiently or economically than with Fortran.

John Backus was once asked by an interviewer what would be the nature of the language running on supercomputers in the year 2000. He replied: "I can't tell you anything about its nature, but I know we will call it 'Fortran.'"

In short, Fortran has a long life ahead of it. And any program, new or old, can profit dramatically from applying the techniques outlined in this book.

3.1
STANDARD FORTRAN

The X3J3 Committee of the American National Standards Institute (ANSI) develops specifications for a standard Fortran language and establishes the interpretation of any program written in the standard form. The latest released standard is known as Fortran 77, and the previous standard is called Fortran 66. The next standard, expected to be released in 1988, is currently named Fortran 8X. Essentially, all of the supercomputer manufacturers provide compilers that can be made to conform to the Fortran 77 standard. Actually, each of the compilers has extensions to Fortran 77 providing additional language features above and beyond the standard. But the user can always force the compiler to recognize and compile only standard Fortran constructs.

Except for some seven-character symbolic names, the examples in this book adhere to the Fortran 77 standard.

3.1.1   Array Layout in Memory

Much of our concern in this book is the optimal handling of array references to and from memory. The ANSI Fortran standard specifies the order in which a compiler must place array elements in memory, and this can have a large effect on machine performance in certain loops.

The dimensions of an array in order from left to right can be thought of as designating row number, column number, plane number, and so forth. An array must be stored in memory in just this order. All of the row elements of column 1 of plane 1 are stored, followed by all of the elements of the second column, and so forth. Remembering that physical memory is treated as one large, single-dimension array, and given the declaration:

```
DIMENSION MATRIX (4, 3)
```

then it will be assigned to memory by the compiler as shown in Figure 3.1. A three-dimensional array such as:

```
DIMENSION BOX (4, 3, 3)
```

has the same layout as depicted for MATRIX for each of its three planes.

Now consider the effect of this layout on the following three DO loops:

```
      DO 3000 J = 1, 3
        DO 3000 I = 1, 4
          MATRIX(I,J) = MATRIX(I,J) + 1.0
3000 CONTINUE

      DO 3010 I = 1, 4
        DO 3010 J = 1, 3
          MATRIX(I,J) = MATRIX(I,J) + 1.0
3010 CONTINUE

      DO 3020 I = 1, 4
        MATRIX(I,I) = MATRIX(I,I) + 1.0
3020 CONTINUE
```

In terms of vectors, if only the inner loops are considered — which is true of many compilers — then loop 3000 operates on three vectors, each of

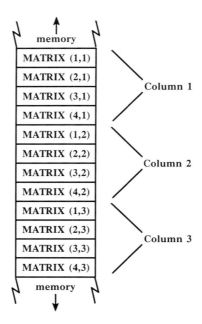

FIGURE 3.1.
Layout of a 2D Array in Memory

length four, and loop 3010 operates on four vectors, each of length three. But the *stride* in loop 3000 is one (the distance in memory between row elements), and the stride in loop 3010 is four (the distance in memory between column elements). Since contiguous vectors are always handled more efficiently than noncontiguous vectors, it is good practice to vary the left-most subscript in inner loops where possible. It is also important (if possible) to have the longest dimension of an array as the left-most to achieve long-vector processing in inner-loop references.

Finally, note the diagonal processing, shown in loop 3020, has a stride of five, which is the length of a column plus one. We shall see in a later section that when nonunit strides are unavoidable, as in diagonal processing, it is sometimes important to adjust the dimension of the arrays to avoid memory-bank conflicts.

In general, given the declaration:

```
DIMENSION ARRAY (L1:U1, L2:U2 . . . , L7:U7)
```

having dimension sizes $D_i = U_i - L_i + 1$, then array element ARRAY $(I1, I2, \ldots , I7)$ is located in memory at

```
address of ARRAY (L1, L2 . . . , L7)

 + (I7-L7) × D1 × D2 × D3 × D4 × D5 × D6
```

$$+ \ (\text{I}6-\text{L}6) \ \times \ \text{D}1 \ \times \ \text{D}2 \ \times \ \text{D}3 \ \times \ \text{D}4 \ \times \ \text{D}5$$

$$+ \ (\text{I}5-\text{L}5) \ \times \ \text{D}1 \ \times \ \text{D}2 \ \times \ \text{D}3 \ \times \ \text{D}4$$

$$+ \ (\text{I}4-\text{L}4) \ \times \ \text{D}1 \ \times \ \text{D}2 \ \times \ \text{D}3$$

$$+ \ (\text{I}3-\text{L}3) \ \times \ \text{D}1 \ \times \ \text{D}2$$

$$+ \ (\text{I}2-\text{L}2) \ \times \ \text{D}1$$

$$+ \ (\text{I}1-\text{L}1)$$

So, in a loop where, say, I5 is varying with an increment of one, and all other subscripts are invariant within the context of the loop, then the stride of the referenced vector is the product of all the lower dimensions, that is, $D1 \times D2 \times D3 \times D4$. For an array dimensioned:

```
DIMENSION HYPER (70, 50, 10, 10, 30)
```

and a loop:

```
      DO 3030 M = 1, N
         HYPER(I,J,K,L,M) = Q * HYPER(I,J,K,L,M)
 3030 CONTINUE
```

then the vector being referenced has a starting address of HYPER (I,J,K,L,1), a length of N, and a stride through memory of $70 \times 50 \times 10 \times 10 = 350{,}000$.

3.2
COMPILERS

A compiler is a computer program that reads our program source code as data and translates it into machine code that can be read and interpreted as instructions and data understandable at the computer's hardware level. The simplest of compilers provides no optimization and performs the steps of our program in exactly the order we have written them. It is valuable to have such compilation available for debugging, since diagnostic messages can then point to the source statement and possibly even the instruction within it that caused a problem.

Once a program is fully debugged and ready for production, it is important to achieve the highest level of optimization possible, since optimization can often provide an order of magnitude in performance improvement over simple compilation. Many machine-independent optimization techniques are employed by all compilers, and these include moving invariant code out of DO loops, evaluating constant expressions, and so forth. Compilers also perform machine-dependent optimizations such as replacing integer exponentiation with multiplication for small powers, instruction shuffling, register scheduling, and — for our purposes the most important — issuance of vector and parallel instructions. It should be obvious that it is to our advantage to learn the optimization details of our target compiler and to use them to our best advantage.

Currently (early 1988), Alliant FX/Fortran is the only compiler with automatic recognition of parallel constructs within Fortran source code. All other parallel machines require other languages or constructs oriented to the expression of communication among the processor nodes, and this is beyond the scope of this text. At best, the burden of parallel analysis is placed entirely on the programmer, with precompilers, compiler directives, and use of machine-specific library routines communicating the parallel constructs to the computer system. Consequently, the bulk of this text is directed at scalar and vector optimization techniques as can be utilized with existing Fortran compilers.

3.2.1   Machine-Independent Optimizations

All compilers search source code for certain constructs that can be optimized by simplifying them, replacing them, or moving them. Writing code that aids the compiler in recognizing such constructs will reduce the number of operations to be performed by our program. We base our examples in a loop context, but many of the techniques can be used to an advantage in serial code as well.

Please note that some of these techniques involve rearranging the order of execution of the operations in our expressions. Our discussion considers only algebraic correctness and does not touch on numeric problems. So before reordering operations, especially if they were written by another programmer, we may have to decide whether the original order is critical to the accuracy of the results due to the precision of representation of floating-point numbers on the target machine.

Invariant-Code Relocation

Compilers search loops for operations involving constants and simple variables not set within the loop (invariants), and move the computation outside of the loop. Note the invariant expressions in the loop 3040:

```
      DO 3040 I = 1, 100
         A(I) = 6.0 + S + X(I)
         B(I) = Y(I) * P / Q
 3040 CONTINUE
```

During optimization, all compilers will perform the invariant code before the loop and reference the results from registers inside the loop as follows:

```
register i = 6.0 + S
register j = P / Q

DO 3041 I = 1, 100
    A(I) = (register i) + X(I)
    B(I) = Y(I) * (register j)
3041 CONTINUE
```

Note that although the original loop specifies 400 floating-point operations, the optimized code executes only 202.

There was a time when compilers did not perform such optimizations, and smart programmers of the time might have coded:

```
TEMP1 = 6.0 + S
TEMP2 = P / Q
DO 3042 I = 1, 100
    A(I) = TEMP1 + X(I)
    B(I) = Y(I) * TEMP2
3042 CONTINUE
```

This is actually slightly less efficient, since it specifies storing and fetching TEMP1 and TEMP2; and not all compilers will optimize this as well as the original. So, believe it or not, it is good practice to put invariant expressions inside the loop, then trust the compiler to optimize them back out.

Sometimes we must help the compiler see invariant code. To this end, we recommend that invariants not be separated by variables. We cannot be sure that a compiler will recognize the invariant code in the loop 3050:

```
DO 3050 I = 1, 100
    A(I) = 6.0 + X(I) + S
    B(I) = P * Y(I) / Q
3050 CONTINUE
```

If we want to be doubly certain that the compiler sees invariant code, we put it in parentheses (a compiler must perform operations inside parentheses before performing those outside the parentheses) as shown in loop 3060:

```
DO 3060 I = 1, 100
    A(I) = (6.0 + S) + X(I)
    B(I) = Y(I) * (P / Q)
3060 CONTINUE
```

A note for the older programmers: Do not be afraid to use unnecessary parentheses to clarify code or to force compilation of instructions in a certain order. About 20 years ago, some compilers generated incorrect code because a programmer used mathematically unnecessary parentheses; parsing has come a long way since then, and we should feel free and safe to use them as we wish.

Constant-Expression Evaluation

When a compiler discovers an invariant expression only involving constants, it evaluates the expression and saves the result in a memory location to be fetched when the program is run—thus eliminating the computation at execution time. This is not only optimal, it can be used to enhance the readability of the program when well-known constants are involved. Thus, loop 3070 is optimized as shown in loop 3071.

```
      DO 3070 I = 1, N
         A(I) = B(I) * 3.14159 * 3.0 / 2.0
3070 CONTINUE

      ( memloc = 3.14159 * 3.0 / 2.0  at compile time )
      DO 3071 I = 1, N
         A(I) = B(I) * memloc
3071 CONTINUE
```

And, although loop 3072 is just as efficient, it is not as readable, and the manual computation of the constant is prone to error.

```
      DO 3072 I = 1, N
         A(I) = B(I) * 4.71239
3072 CONTINUE
```

Common Subexpression Elimination

Compilers also search for repeated expressions that can be safely computed once with subsequent occurrences satisfied from a register. Thus, in loop 3080, a compiler will recognize both T(I) * S(I) and X(I) / Y(I) as common subexpressions and optimize them as shown in loop 3081:

```
      DO 3080 I = 1, N
         A(I) = C(I) + T(I) * S(I)
         B(I) = P * X(I) / Y(I)
         C(I) = Q * X(I) / Y(I)
         D(I) = T(I) * S(I) + B(I) / C(I)
3080 CONTINUE
```

Optimized:

```
      DO 3081 I = 1, N
         register i = T(I) * S(I)
         register j = X(I) / Y(I)
         A(I) = C(I) + (register i)
         B(I) = P * (register j)
         C(I) = Q * (register j)
         D(I) = (register i) + B(I) / C(I)
3081 CONTINUE
```

Again, while this optimization technique is now universal, there was a time in the dark ages of computing when this was not done, and the best programmers would write

```
DO 3082 I = 1, N
     TMULTS = T(I) * S(I)
     XOVERY = X(I) / Y(I)
     A(I) = C(I) + TMULTS
     B(I) = P * XOVERY
     C(I) = Q * XOVERY
     D(I) = TMULTS + B(I) / C(I)
3082 CONTINUE
```

As we might guess, this is now less than optimal, since some compilers might be forced to store the values into the variables TMULTS and XOVERY— something that does not occur in the original.

To aid a compiler in recognizing common subexpressions, use the same techniques regarding code arrangement and parentheses as outlined in the section on invariant code. Thus, a compiler might miss the common subexpressions in loop 3090:

```
DO 3090 I = 1, N
     A(I) = C(I) * T(I) * S(I)
     B(I) = X(I) * P / Y(I)
     C(I) = X(I) * Q / Y(I)
     D(I) = T(I) * S(I) * B(I) / C(I)
3090 CONTINUE
```

but would not miss them in loop 3091:

```
DO 3091 I = 1, N
     A(I) = C(I) * ( T(I) * S(I) )
     B(I) = P * ( X(I) / Y(I) )
     C(I) = Q * ( X(I) / Y(I) )
     D(I) = ( T(I) * S(I) ) * B(I) / C(I)
3091 CONTINUE
```

Unneeded Store Elimination

If the same variable or array element appears on the left side of the equals sign more than once within a loop, the compiler will optimize by storing only the final setting. Consider for example loop 3100:

```
DO 3100 I = 1, N
     TEMP(I) = X(I) + Y(I)
     W(I) = Z(I) ** 2 + TEMP(I)
     R(I) = W(I) / TEMP(I)
3100 CONTINUE
```

Assuming that TEMP is a scratch array whose values are unneeded, then the following will be more efficiently handled by a compiler:

```
DO 3101 I = 1, N
     R(I) = X(I) + Y(I)
     W(I) = Z(I) ** 2 + R(I)
     R(I) = W(I) / R(I)
3101 CONTINUE
```

which will be optimized as:

```
      DO 3102 I = 1, N
      register j = X(I) + Y(I)
          W(I) = Z(I) ** 2 + register j
          R(I) = W(I) / register j
 3102 CONTINUE
```

thereby eliminating N memory references.

3.2.2   Machine-Dependent Optimizations

These techniques are concerned with the optimal use of the underlying machine resources: registers, functional units, and the like.

Instruction Scheduling

A compiler typically views a routine as a series of "optimization blocks" of source code statements within which it tries to issue instructions in an order that attains the greatest overlap of execution while assuring correct results. Fetches from memory are often the most expensive operations (in time). So they are scheduled to occur well in advance of the operations in which the data is involved, in order that the fetch time can be overlapped with unrelated computation.

Most computers can perform only one occurrence of an arithmetic operation at a time, so, for example, if two multiplies occur in a row, as in

```
   X(I) = Y(I) * Z(I) * W(I) / (A(I) + B(I))
```

then, if possible, the compiler will schedule the instruction to perform $Y(I) * Z(I)$, then issue $A(I) + B(I)$, then return to issue the multiply by $W(I)$. This technique can be applied across statements so that operations are done as soon as possible with maximal concurrency.

A programmer can choose an order of operations that enhances the compiler's ability to perform this kind of optimization, as in Horner's rule for polynomial evaluation. Consider the following conventionally coded polynomial:

```
   P = A0 + A1 * X + A2 * X**2 + A3 * X**3 + A4 * X**4
```

Now a smart compiler can fetch X to a register, compute X**2 to another register, use that to compute X**3, and so forth. This reduces the number of operations to produce the powers of X, but it still requires two multiplies in a row for all terms beyond A1*X. Horner's rule suggests that polynomials be entirely factored in X:

```
   P = A0 + (X * (A1 + X * (A2 + X * (A3 + X * A4))))
```

Not only does Horner's rule further reduce the number of multiplies, but it naturally schedules an overlap of adds, multiplies, and fetches (of the Ai), which almost guarantees that the compiler will generate optimal code. A very smart compiler might be programmed to recognize polynomials and then invoke Horner's rule. But it should be easy to imagine that, in general, a compiler's ability to perform such transformations must be limited if only to keep compilation time itself at an acceptable level. Therefore, a programmer should write expressions and even groups of statements in a manner that alternates independent operations as much as possible.

Operator Strength Reduction

Wherever results will be exactly the same, compilers will usually replace costly operations with equivalent, less-expensive ones. Thus, integer divide by a power of 2, as in

```
IOVER4 = I / 4
```

will be replaced with an operation that shifts off the two right-most bits of I, instead of using the divide functional unit. This might take two clock cycles instead of 20 or more. We hinted in the previous section that exponentiation to an integer power will be treated as successive multiplication up to the point that multiplies become more expensive than invoking an exponentiation routine on a given machine. This is usually in the range of powers five to ten. This is typically not done for floating-point exponentiation, so we should always write

```
X**2
```

instead of:

```
X**2.0
```

The first will probably run ten times faster than the second.

Furthermore, when variables are used for powers, most compilers will call exponentiation routines, since they cannot know the values at compile time. Consider, for example, loop 3110:

```
      DO 3110 J = 1, NDIM
        DO 3110 I = 1, N
          A(I) = A(I) + X(I)**(J-1) * Y(I)**(J-1)
 3110 CONTINUE
```

If we know that NDIM is always three, and always will be, then we can realize a significant speedup by expressing this directly:

```
      DO 3111 I = 1, N
        A(I) = A(I) + 1.0 + X(I) * Y(I) * (1.0 + X(I) * Y(I))
 3111 CONTINUE
```

The original loop demanded 3*N calls to an exponentiation routine, but the rewritten loop has no explicit exponentiation. Furthermore, the original specified fetching the elements of A, X, and Y three times, but the restruc-

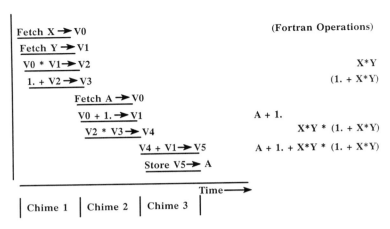

FIGURE 3.2.
Chime Diagram of Loop 3111

tured loop fetches them only once. Finally, recognition of the common subexpression X(I) * Y(I) by the compiler will eliminate one of the multiply instructions, so that alternating adds and multiplies will overlap. The technique used to eliminate the outer loop on J is called "unrolling" and has many applications we will explore in later sections.

A chime diagram of loop 3111 on the Cray X-MP is shown in Figure 3.2.

Register Assignment

Registers are recognized by a compiler as a precious resource, and every attempt is made to use this very fast memory efficiently. To this end, heavily used local variables might be assigned permanently to registers. And we have shown earlier that registers are used to hold common subexpression evaluations to avoid redundant computation.

A local variable is a scalar variable that is neither a dummy argument nor is used as an actual argument nor does it appear in a common block. In other words, its entire use is local to the subprogram in which it appears. Such a variable may be assigned to a register where it can be manipulated very quickly; it need never be stored into or fetched from memory. Some programmers create a common block containing a number of such "scratch" variables, so that the memory space can be shared by all subprograms; this inhibits a compiler from using the register assignment. If the memory savings are not needed, such variables should be restored to true local status to allow more effective use of the registers.

Note that the previous discussion applies to local variables, not to local arrays, which are always memory-based.

A programmer can use knowledge of the number of registers available to estimate the performance of a DO loop or even a compiler's ability to optimize it at all. Very short loops give a compiler very little to optimize; overly long loops can overwhelm the register capacity, forcing the compiler to use temporary memory space as pseudoregisters; extremely long loops might inhibit optimization entirely.

Short Loops

Several short loops of the same length, especially if they share variables and expressions, should be combined to provide the compiler with more opportunity to use the machine's registers effectively. For example:

```
      DO 3121 I = 1, N
 3121 X(I) = A(I) + B(I) / ( D(I) + S * C(I) )

      DO 3122 I = 1, N
 3122 Y(I) = X(I) + A(I) * B(I)

      DO 3123 I = 1, N
 3123 X(I) = X(I) / ( D(I) + S * C(I) )
```

is much better written as:

```
      DO 3124 I = 1, N
         X(I) = A(I) + B(I) / ( D(I) + S * C(I) )
         Y(I) = X(I) + A(I) * B(I)
         X(I) = X(I) / ( D(I) + S * C(I) )
 3124 CONTINUE
```

In this form, the compiler can fetch the values of A, B, C, and D only once, then reuse them from registers; the common subexpression $D(I) + S * C(I)$ can be calculated and reused, the first setting of X(I) need not be stored, and the value of X(I) can be reused from a register in the last two equations.

Long Loops

Let us now estimate, for a Cray computer with eight vector registers, how many registers are needed for the duration of loop 3124.

In the execution of the first line, vector registers are needed to fetch A, B, C, and D, and each dyadic operation requires two registers as operands and one for results. But, some of the registers may be reused. For example, the registers holding the values of D and C are no longer needed once the common subexpression $D(I) + S * C(I)$ is computed. So upon completion of the first equation, four active vector registers hold the values of X, A, B, and the common subexpression — all of which are needed for further computation. Upon completing the second equation, the registers holding A and B are no longer needed. Only the registers containing X and the common subexpression are needed for the final equation.

In other words, a compiler can probably perform all of the loop's computation using only four or five vector registers, so an even longer loop with more computation can be optimized easily. Consider loop 3130:

```
    DO 3130 I = 1, N
      X(I) = A(I) + B(I) / ( D(I) + S * C(I) )
      Y(I) = X(I) + A(I) * B(I)
      W(I) = A(I) * B(I) + C(I) * Y(I) + D(I)
      X(I) = X(I) / ( D(I) + S * C(I) )
3130 CONTINUE
```

Here, the added equation $(W(I) = \ldots)$ has a subexpression $A(I) * B(I)$ that has been already calculated in the second equation, and the same equation also requires B, C, D, and Y for further computation. A compiler trying to optimize register usage would find that at the end of the second equation it would like to hold onto the registers containing A, B, C, D, X, Y, $A(I) * B(I)$ and $D(I) + S * C(I)$ — eight registers in all. At this point we could imagine that the compiler would abandon one of the registers in favor of refetching or recomputing its value later in the loop. This is hardly the way compilers actually "think" about register allocation, but it is a good exercise for a programmer trying to understand how to form loops that utilize most of the computer's resources without overtaxing them. Later in this chapter we will discuss how to choose points in very long loops at which to split them into several moderate-sized loops.

3.3
VECTORIZATION

Vectorization causes a computer to compute with vector rather than scalar instructions. When applied to a compiler, vectorization means that the compiler is capable of generating vector machine code; when attributed to a programmer, it means that he or she has written constructs recognizable by the compiler as vectorizable.

Any given compiler provides explicit and implicit vectorization. Within the context of ANSI 77 Fortran all vectorization is implicit, and any explicit vectorization is necessarily an extension to the language. The next standard version of Fortran, presently known as Fortran 8X, contains many explicit array operations that can be easily interpreted as vector instructions.

3.3.1   Explicit Vectorization

Compilers on supercomputers provide programmers with certain constructs that have only vector interpretations. The use of these constructs is known as explicit vectorization. We also include in this classification the use of machine-specific vector library routines when called from a Fortran program.

Compiler Directives

All of the compilers provide a set of special comment cards ignored by any other compiler but interpreted for user information by the target compiler. A subset of these directives is explicitly concerned with vectorization of DO loops. They were first introduced in Cray's CFT compilers, and there have the form:

```
CDIR$ directive [,directive. . .]
```

"Directive" might be simple, like VECTOR, indicating that the compiler is to begin to vectorize loops, or might be something more complicated, such as IVDEP, meaning "ignore vector dependencies." The use of directives will be introduced in examples after we have developed the terminology of vectorization.

Fortran 8X

Although not yet released as a standard, several compilers have incorporated some of the features of Fortran 8X, as proposed by ANSI's X3J3 committee. Control Data Corporation's Fortran 200, Cray's CFT77, and Alliant's FX/Fortran have all provided "array section syntax" as an extension to their Fortran 77 implementation. Assignment statements involving array section syntax are immediately interpretable as a series of vector operations by these compilers.

An "array section" is derived from an array by specifying "subscript triplets" in some of the subscript positions of the array. A subscript triplet has the form:

```
i : j : k
```

where i is the initial subscript value, j is the bound of the final subscript value, and k is the subscript stride or increment.

The initial and final bound values must be within the dimension of the array; the stride may be any nonzero value. It is simplest to think of a subscript triplet as DO control values. For example the array assignment statement

```
A(1:20:2) = B(1:20:2)
```

may be interpreted as

```
      DO 3140 I = 1, 20, 2
        A(I) = B(I)
3140 CONTINUE
```

Any or all of the subscript values may be omitted from a subscript triplet:

i:j   means from i to j with a stride of one
:j   means from the lower-dimension bound to j
i: means from i to the upper-dimension bound
:   means from lower to upper bound

Finally, note that an array name appearing with no subscript expressions whatsoever implies the entire array.
Given:

```
DIMENSION A(100)
```

then

```
A(1:100:1)

A(1:100 )

A( :100 )

A(1: )

A( : )

A
```

all have the same interpretation — that is, the entire array.

Next, note that a subscript triplet can appear in any subscript position of a multidimensioned array, thus specifying a section of the whole array, often with a different shape and size than the original. Thus, given:

```
DIMENSION X(100, 50, 25)
```

then

```
X(1:50, 17, 11:25:2)
```

specifies a subarray of two dimensions whose shape is [50,8].

Whenever array sections are involved in an assignment statement then they must conform in shape and size. This means that for each array reference containing subscript triplets, there must be the same number of triplets; and in order from left to right, corresponding triplets must be the same size. Scalar variables, constants, and array references not containing triplets always conform in shape to any array section — that is, they are treated as an array of the appropriate shape with the same value at every element.

Here are some clarifying examples:

```
DIMENSION A(100), B(-1:98), X(100, 50, 25)

DIMENSION Y(100, 100, 10, 70)
```

Comment: M, N, P, Q, R are scalar variables.

```
A( : ) = 1.0
```

C sets all elements of A to 1.0.

```
B( :10) = P + Q
```

C sets elements B(−1:10) to the invariant P + Q

```
X(:,N,1) = A(:) + B(:)
```

C sets the Nth column in the first plane of X
C to A(1:100) + B(-1:98).

$$X(M:N, \quad 1:10, \quad 1:20) = Y(1, \quad M:N, \quad 1:10, \quad 41:60)$$

C sets a 3-D subsection of X to a 3-D subsection of Y.

Multidimensioned array sections such as in the last example can be interpreted as a DO loop nest with the left-most triplet as the inner loop and the rightmost triplet as the outermost loop. Loop interpretations of all the preceding examples follow:

```
      DO 3150 I = 1, 100
         A(I) = 1.0
3150  CONTINUE

      DO 3160 I = -1, 10
         B(I) = P + Q
3160  CONTINUE

      DO 3170 I = 1, 100
         X(I, N, 1) = A(I) + B(I-2)
3170  CONTINUE

      DO 3180 K = 1, 20
        DO 3180 J = 1, 10
          DO 3180 I = M, N
             X(I, J, K) = Y(1, I, J, K+40)
3180  CONTINUE
```

In the general form of an array-section assignment

array section = expression

it is important to note that "expression" is fully evaluated for all elements before any assignment is made to the left side array section. Because of this, there can be no feedback of data from the left to the right as in certain DO loops such as:

```
      DO 3190 I = 2, N
         A(I) = A(I-1) + A(I+1)
3190  CONTINUE
```

The following is *not* equivalent to loop 3190:

```
A(2:N) = A(1:N-1) + A(3:N+1)
```

A loop interpretation of the preceding array assignment statement is

```
      DO 3200 I = 2, N
         TEMP(I) = A(I-1) + A(I+1)
3200  CONTINUE

      DO 3201 I = 2,N
         A(I) = TEMP(I)
3201  CONTINUE
```

To repeat, the feedback of values inherent in loop 3190 cannot be written in an array-section assignment statement. The right side of the expression is always fully evaluated for all elements using *old* values before any new values are stored on the left. Feedback is fully discussed in a later section on recursion in loops.

Vector-mask operations are also directly specifiable in array syntax using the WHERE statement and WHERE blocks. These constructs derive directly from the IF statements and IF blocks of Fortran 77 and have the following forms:

```
WHERE ( mask expression) array = expression

WHERE ( mask expression)

   array = expression

      .  .  .

ENDWHERE

WHERE ( mask expression)

   array = expression

      .  .  .

ELSEWHERE

   array = expression

      .  .  .

ENDWHERE
```

Examples of each of the three forms and an accompanying loop interpretation follow:

```
WHERE (A(1:N) .GT. B(1:N)) A(1:N) = X
```

is the same as

```
      DO 3210 I = 1, N
         IF (A(I) .GT. B(I)) A(I) = X
3210 CONTINUE

WHERE (A(1:N) .GT. EPSLON)

   A(1:N) = A(1:N) / 2.0

ENDWHERE
```

is the same as

```
      DO 3220 I = 1, N
         IF (A(I) .GT. EPSLON) THEN
            A(I) = A(I) / 2.0
         ENDIF
3220 CONTINUE
```

```
WHERE (A(1:N) .GT. B(1:N))

    A(1:N) = X

ELSEWHERE

    A(1:N) = B(1:N)

ENDWHERE
```

is the same as

```
        DO 3230 I = 1, N
            IF (A(I) .GT. B(I)) THEN
                A(I) = X
            ELSE
                A(I) = B(I)
            ENDIF
3230    CONTINUE
```

All of the preceding WHERE constructs can be vectorized immediately and unambiguously.

Finally, note that all of the Fortran 77 intrinsic functions have been extended to accept array arguments, so the following can be written:

```
A(1:N) = EXP ( SQRT (A(1:N)))
```

which is the same as

```
        DO 3240 I = 1, N
            A(I) = EXP ( SQRT (A(I)))
3240    CONTINUE
```

The most important attribute of Fortran 8X array assignment statements is that they can be explicitly interpreted as vector operations.

CYBER 205 Explicit Vector Syntax

More than fifteen years ago CDC defined a vector syntax for the STAR-100, and it is still available on the CYBER 205 and ETA 10. It is a unique syntax for assignment statements, vector functions, and in-line assembly language, by which every machine instruction may be invoked directly from a Fortran routine. Assignment statements specify vectors rather than the array sections of Fortran 8X. An explicit vector has a starting array element, a length, and a fixed stride of one. It has the form:

```
array ( starting subscript ; length)
```

Given

```
DIMENSION A(100), B(100, 50), C(100, 50, 25)
```

Then a vector assignment statement could be

```
A(1 ; 100) = B(1,1 ; 100) + C(1,10,17 ; 100)
```

A form of the WHERE statement already described is also available to perform vector mask operations with these vector assignment statements. All of the standard intrinsic functions have special vector versions, as in:

```
A( 1 ; 100 ) = VSQRT ( A( 1 ; 100); 100 )
```

and many machine instructions such as vector average, vector merge, and vector polynomial are provided as vector functions as well.

As with Fortran 8X array syntax, the most important feature of CYBER 205 vector syntax is that it is a direct specification of vector instructions. Unlike DO loops — which may or may not vectorize, depending on a great many factors — vector syntax guarantees vector instructions.

Machine-Specific Library Routines

Each of the supercomputer vendors provides a number of Fortran-callable library routines, highly optimized and vectorized, and often written in assembly language. We highly recommend that programmers investigate the use of such routines in important CPU-intensive regions of their programs. But, keep in mind that such use reduces the transportability of the source code to other vendors' systems.

3.3.2   Implicit Vectorization

Compiling DO loops into vector instructions is by far the most common form of vectorization. It is implicit because by definition a DO loop is a specification of an iterative series of scalar operations. It is fortuitous if a compiler can recognize that the same computation can be performed with vector instructions. We shall see that a programmer cannot always be sure whether a complicated loop will vectorize; often, a compilation listing must be scanned to determine how the loop was handled. To further discuss implicit vectorization, we must first establish some terminology.

Vectorization Terminology

In this section we develop a working vocabulary of terms to analyze and discuss the constructs that can appear as standard Fortran DO loops and how these constructs affect a compiler's ability to vectorize the loops.

Constant-Increment Variable.   A constant-increment variable (CIV) is a scalar variable whose value is incremented or decremented by a fixed amount on *every* iteration of a DO loop. All of the scalar variables in loop

3250 are CIVs.

```
DO 3250 I = 1, 100
     J = I - 5
     K = K + 1
     L = 6 - K
     M = 3 * I + 4
     P = P + 2.0
     A(I) = B(J) * C(K) + D(L) * E(M) / P + F(N)
     N = N + 1
3250 CONTINUE
```

Assuming that each of the variables has an initial value of zero, then the sequence of values attained within the loop is

Sequence	Increment
$I =$ 1, 2, . . . , 100	1
$J = -4, -3, \ldots , \quad 95$	1
$K =$ 1, 2, . . . , 100	1
$L =$ 5, 4, . . . , -94	-1
$M =$ 7, 10, . . . , 304	3
$N =$ 1, 2, . . . , 100	1
$P =$ 2., 4., . . . , 200.	2

The use of integer variables in this manner is so important to vectorization that they are separately designated "constant-increment integers" or CIIs. Their use as array subscripts often results in a "vector array reference."

Given that "II" is any integer variable and "IP" is any previously defined CII, then any of the following are valid for defining CIIs in a DO loop:

II = II ± invariant expression
II = invariant expression + II
II = [± invariant expression *] IP [± invariant expression]
II = [± invariant expression] [± invariant expression *] IP

By definition, the DO loop index variable is always a CII.

Constant-increment variables such as P in loop 3250 can be treated as vectors of values at execution time, with the last value attained saved in the variable at loop termination. This use of scalar variables will be developed further in later sections.

Vector Array Reference. In a DO loop, an array reference having one subscript expression as a linear function of a single CII. All other subscript expressions, being invariant, can be treated as a vector. A linear CII subscript expression is defined as:

[± invariant expression *] CII [± invariant expression]

As a simple example, all of the array references in loop 3250 can be handled as vector array references. Other examples follow:

```
DIMENSION W(100), X(100, 50), Y(50, 1500, 2), Z(1000)
     . . .
DO 3260 I = 1, N
     J = 3 * I + 3 - N
     K = L * J - 5
     X(I, N) = Y(M, 5*J, L) + Z(K-4) / W(I)
3260 CONTINUE
```

Remember that a vector has a starting address, a length, and a constant stride through memory. A compiler is able to derive that information at execution time for the array references X, Y, and Z in loop 3260. Given that the integer variables L, M, and N are all defined before the loop is executed, then the vectors are defined as follows:

Array	Starting Address	Length	Stride
W	W(1)	N	1
X	X(1, N)	N	1
Y	Y(M, 30 − 5*N)	N	750
Z	Z((6 − N)*L − 9)	N	3*L

The stride of 750 in Y is derived from the facts that the subscript expression itself, 5*J, has a stride of 5*3 = 15, and the stride through memory is in the second dimension of Y; so it specifies striding across columns of length 50, and 15*50 = 750.

Compilers vary in their ability to detect linear subscript expressions. If there is ever any doubt, the compiler will resort to indirect address vectors described in the next section.

Indirect-Address Vectors.   An indirect-address vector is a list of values in an array in memory that is not explicitly characterized by a constant stride but whose subscript expressions themselves are vectorizable. Loops 2180 and 2200 from Chapter 2 are examples of indirect-address vectors:

```
DO 2180 I = 1, 64
     A(IA(I)) = B(IB(I)) + C(IC(I))
2180 CONTINUE

DO 2200 I = 1,N
     J = I * I / (I + 1)
     K = MOD (J, 10) + 1
     L = ISQRT (IA(I) * IB(I))
     M = 6 - M
     A(J) = (B(K) + C(L)) * D(M)
2200 CONTINUE
```

In loop 2180, the indirect-address indexes are explicit and should be obvious; in loop 2200, the compiler must cause the vectors of indexes to be computed at execution time. This same technique is used by compilers anytime that they cannot determine whether a subscript expression has a constant stride.

Indirect-address fetching of data from memory is called a "gather" operation. Indirect storing is called a "scatter" operation.

Scalar Temporaries or Pseudovectors. Whenever a scalar variable is set equal to a vectorizable expression, the entire expression can be performed in a vector register or a temporary vector in memory. At loop termination, the last value computed can be stored into the scalar variable. Example:

```
      DO 3270 I = 1, N
        SCA = A(I) * B(I) + SQRT (X(I)**2 + Y(I)**2)
        R(I) = SCA * Y(I)
        Z(I) = (D(I) + E(I)) / SCA
 3270 CONTINUE
```

Here, the scalar temporary SCA is transparently promoted to a vector by the compiler. That is, the instructions generated are the same as if SCA were an array, *except* only the value computed in the Nth iteration is stored into memory, rather than all of the values computed. Some compilers are smart enough to determine whether it is even necessary to save the last value. For instance, if SCA is not in COMMON, not a dummy argument, and not referenced outside the loop, then there is no need to save it. Many compilers provide directives that allow the programmer to choose or prevent "last-value-saving."

The judicious use of scalar temporaries, or "pseudovectors," can reduce the number of memory references needed within a loop. Some problems with their use will be discussed in the following section on recursion.

Note that invariant array elements within a loop have the same characteristics as scalars, so a compiler can apply the same optimization techniques. So, for example, in loop 3280, J is invariant in the inner loop on I. A vector register holds the values of X(J,J) * T(I); at the end of each execution of the inner loop, the last value X(J,J) * T(N) is saved in A(J).

```
      DO 3280 J = 1,M
        DO 3280 I = 1,N
          A(J)   = X(J,J) * T(I)
          Y(I,J) = X(I,J) / A(J)
 3280 CONTINUE
```

We will often refer to such invariant array elements as "array constants." It is not their value but their subscript expressions that are constant or invariant for the duration of an inner loop.

Recursion. "Data dependency" among Fortran statements is a term indicating that a variable stored into in one statement is subsequently used by another statement. Thus, in the following, the second statement depends on the first, and they must be executed in the order in which they are written:

```
S = T + U

X = S * Y
```

In the vectorization of DO loops we concern ourselves with recursive data dependencies, in which a statement in the loop is data dependent on itself or on a statement that *succeeds* it in the loop. One of the simplest examples is:

```
     DO 3290 I = 2, N
        A(I) = A(I-1) + B(I)
3290 CONTINUE
```

Let A' indicate newly set values of the array A, and write out several iterations of the loop:

```
A'(2) = A (1) + B(1)

A'(3) = A'(2) + B(2)

        . . .

A'(N) = A'(N-1) + B(N)
```

Note that the output from the first iteration, A'(2), is input to the second iteration — that is, its address "recurs" in the second iteration. Naturally, this is called a recurrence or recursion. It is sometimes also referred to as data feedback, again for obvious reasons. This condition is of extreme importance, because it makes vectorization of the loop impossible. Remember that to vectorize a loop such as:

```
     DO 3300 I = 1, N
        A(I) = B(I) + C(I)
3300 CONTINUE
```

we want to fetch all of the elements of the vector B and all of the elements of C, then add them together and store them into A. The recurrence in loop 3290 prevents the fetching of A, because its elements contain all *old* values. The new values can be derived only by executing the loop iterations one at a time in *scalar* mode. Some compilers can recognize such single-dimension recursion and optimize the scalar instructions. But the execution rate is typically a factor of three or four less than the vector execution of loop 3300.

Single-dimension recursion is the only condition that absolutely prevents vectorization of arithmetic operations in a DO loop. It is important to understand the nature of recursion, and that it is a necessary and unavoidable part of some algorithms. In later sections we will demonstrate that when recursion occurs in a multidimension problem, often there are techniques allowing us to vectorize the important loops.

Further Recursion Involving Arrays. To restate the definition of recursion: Any address set in one iteration of a DO loop and subsequently referenced in another iteration is a recurrence. Recursion in any one dimension of an array prevents vectorization of the settings and references within that dimension. Sometimes the recursion is not directly determinable by a compiler. But if *potential* for recursion exists, the compiler must either avoid vectorization or must add extra instructions to resolve any ambiguities at execution time. Loop 3310 contains such ambiguities.

```
          DO 3310 I = 1, N
            A(I) = C(I) * B(IB(I))
            B(I) = X(I) * Y(I)
            D(I) = E(I) / A(I+L)
     3310 CONTINUE
```

The arrays A and B are each being indexed in a manner that makes it difficult to determine whether recursion will take place. Array A(I) is being set in the first statement, and A(I+L) is being referenced in the third. If $0 < L < N$, then at least one and as many as N-1 addresses set in the first statement will be referenced in the third on subsequent iterations. For L not in that range, no feedback occurs. The ability of the compiler to determine the value of L either at compile time or execution time will decide whether the use of A in the loop can ever be vectorized. If the value or sign of L remains ambiguous, then the loop must be executed in scalar mode.

Any time that an array is both set and referenced in the same loop and the subscript expressions differ by an indeterminate value—that is, *ambiguous subscripting*—then the potential for recursion exists. Compilers can sometimes resolve the ambiguities; programmers can almost always resolve them with compiler directives. Examples of this appear in a later section.

The indirect addressing of B in loop 3310 is even more of a challenge. From a compiler's viewpoint, the values of the indexes IB(I) might actually repeat earlier values of the loop index I, so the use of B in the loop must be handled with scalar instructions. A compiler can rarely resolve such ambiguity, but a programmer often can resolve it with a compiler directive, leading to vectorization where appropriate.

In general, whenever an array is both set and referenced in the same loop and any of the subscript expressions involve indirect addressing, the compiler will generate scalar instructions unless the programmer informs it that there is no recursion. Note that even when the indexes are the same, as in loop 3320, there is still potential for recursion.

```
          DO 3320 I = 1, 3
            A(IA(I)) = A(IA(I)) + B(I)
     3320 CONTINUE
```

Consider:

I	IA(I)
1	1
2	2
3	1

Unrolling the loop in scalar mode and designating "new" values as A':

```
A'(1) = A(1) + B(1)

A'(2) = A(2) + B(2)

A'(1) = A'(1) + B(3)
```

It should be clear that the value set in iteration 1 recursively feeds back into iteration 3. Attempting to vectorize the loop would result in:

```
A'(1) = A(1) + B(1)

A'(2) = A(2) + B(2)

A'(1) = A(1) + B(3)
```

There is no feedback, because all of the values of A are fetched on the right side before any are stored on the left. Compilers are aware of this potential problem, so they force such usage to be performed in scalar mode unless otherwise directed by the programmer.

Further Recursion Involving Scalars.   Any time a scalar variable or array constant is referenced before it is set within a loop, it results in recursion. We refer to such variables as "wrap-around scalars," and their usage is termed "scalar recursion." Loops 3330 through 3332 contain examples of scalar recursion.

```
      XSUM = 0.
      DO 3330 I = 1, N
         XSUM = XSUM + X(I)
 3330 CONTINUE

      DO 3331 J = 1 , N
         DO 3331 I = 1 , N
          A(I,J) = 0.
          DO 3331 K = 1, N
             A(I,J) = A(I,J) + B(I,K) * C(K,J)
 3331 CONTINUE

      XMAX = X(1)
      YMAX = Y(1)
```

```
     DO 3332 I = 2,N
       XMAX = AMAX1 ( XMAX, X(I))
       IF (YMAX .GT. Y(I) ) YMAX = Y(I)
3332 CONTINUE
```

Loops 3330, 3331, and 3332 each contain an example of a "reduction-function scalar." A reduction function processes a vector of values and reduces it to a single scalar value as a result. Loop 3330 computes the sum of the elements of the array X, placing the answer in XSUM. Loop 3331 is the classic way to write the matrix multiply in Fortran, with the inner loop expressing a dot product of a row of B and a column of C, the answer going to a single element of A. Loop 3332 contains two ways of finding the value of the maximum in an array.

Most compilers can recognize and optimize the computation involved in the following reduction functions as they appear in DO loops

scalar = scalar + vectorizable expression
scalar = scalar − vectorizable expression
scalar = scalar * vectorizable expression
scalar = scalar / vectorizable expression
scalar = MAX (scalar, vectorizable expression)
scalar = MIN (scalar, vectorizable expression)
IF (scalar .relop. vectorizable expression)
        scalar = vectorizable expression

where

MAX/MIN   represent the whole family of related Fortran-intrinsic functions
.relop.   is one of .GT., .GE., .LT., .LE.

The vectorizable expressions can always be computed with vector instructions. The actual reduction of the expression to the final value usually involves some scalar code. So even on machines that have specific machine instructions for such operations as dot product, the result rate for reduction functions is somewhat lower than for pure vector operations. The most important thing to know about reduction function scalars is that although the compilers can optimize the generation of the *final* result, they cannot generate any of the intermediate results except by executing the computation in pure scalar mode. This means that the reduction-function scalar may not appear in any other statement of the loop if optimization is desired. For example, consider loop 3340:

```
     XSUM = 0.
     DO 3340 I = 1, N
        XSUM = XSUM + X(I)
        Y(I) = XSUM * Z(I)
3340 CONTINUE
```

In loop 3340 Y(I) is a function of the *partial* sums of X. There is no efficient way to compute this using vector instructions on any machine, so the loop will be executed in scalar mode.

Loop 3350 represents a different kind of wrap-around scalar.

```
      TOP = 0.
      DO 3350 I = 1, N
         BOTTOM = TOP
         TOP     = X(I) * Y(I)
         Z(I)    = (TOP - BOTTOM) * P(I) + TOP**2
 3350 CONTINUE
```

Here, the scalar BOTTOM is being used to hold the value of TOP from the previous iteration of the loop. Together, BOTTOM and TOP act as a moving interval or window within the expression X(I) * Y(I). Neither scalar is accumulating information from all iterations, as with the preceding reduction functions. In a later section we will show that all such cases of "holding scalars" can be eliminated by *substitution* of their defining expressions or by *promotion* to a newly defined array of their values — thus allowing the loop to fully vectorize.

Finally, wrap-around scalar recursion can result from the scalar being defined conditionally, as in loop 3360.

```
      SCA = 0.
      DO 3360 I = 1, N
         IF (A(I) .GT. 0.) THEN
            SCA = X(I) * Y(I)
         ENDIF
         Z(I) = SCA + B(I)
 3360 CONTINUE
```

On any iteration when the condition A(I) .GT. 0. is false, SCA is not set, and the value used to define Z(I) wraps around from the previous iteration. In general, we cannot predict for which indexes a condition will be true or false. So it is almost impossible to create the list of values assumed by SCA except by using scalar instructions. We shall see later than in some cases there will be a payoff for computing all the values in a separate scalar loop and saving them in a newly defined array for reference in subsequent loops.

Problems

1. Knowing that a particular machine has 64 banks and a memory-bank cycle time of four clock cycles, which of the following array references will incur memory bank conflicts?

```
      DIMENSION A(1024,1024), B(8,1024,64), C(1025,1024)
```

. . .

a. A(:,6)
b. A(6,:)
c. A(1:1024:16,6)

    e. B(7,:,64)
    f. B(7,1:1024:4,5)
    g. C(6,:)
    h. C(1:1025:32,:)

(Note: it is interesting that g will probably run much faster than b.)

2. Conversion of Fortran 8X to efficient vector code can be difficult. On a register-to-register machine, the most effective means of execution is to stripmine across a large number of related operations, as are often found in a substantive DO loop. Consider the following examples:

```
DIMENSION  A(200), B(200), C(200)
                . . .
```

```
a)    Fortran 8X                    Fortran 77

      A = B + 2.                    DO 10 I=1,200
      C = A*B - 3*B                 A(I)=B(I)+2.
                                    C(I)=A(I)*B(I)-3*B(I)
                             10     CONTINUE


b)    Fortran 8X                    Fortran 77

      A(1:199)=B(1:199)+2           DO 20 I=2,200
      C(2:200)=A(2:200)            A(I-1)=B(I-1)+2.
      *         *B(2:200)          C(I)=A(I)*B(I)-3*B(I)
      *         -3.*B(2:200)   20   CONTINUE
```

Are the Fortran 8X and Fortran 77 versions of each example equivalent? Many compilers may have to stripmine across each statement of the Fortran 8X code if they lack the necessary analysis to determine if statements can be combined in the looping structure.

3. Given that IA(:) = 1, will a compiler treat the reference A(IA(I)) as a vector or as an array constant if it appears in a DO loop?

4. In the following DO loops, what values of SCA will be saved in memory at the termination of each loop.

```
a)        DO 10  I = 1, N
            SCA   = A(I) + B(I)
            C(I)  = SCA + D(I)**2
     10     CONTINUE


b)        SCA = 0.0
          DO 20 I = 1, N
            C(I)  = SCA + D(I)**2
            SCA   = A(I) + B(I)
     20     CONTINUE
```

```
c)          DO 30  I = 1, N
            IF (A(I) .GT. EPS) THEN
              SCA  = A(I) + B(I)
              C(I) = SCA + D(I)**2
            ENDIF
     30     CONTINUE
```

5. On a Cray computer with a vector register length of 64, is the following DO loop recursive if:

```
            DO 10  I=1,N
            A(I+L) = A(I) * X(I) + SCA
     10     CONTINUE
              a)  L = 1?  b) L = ⁻1? c) L = 64?
```

On the NEC SX2 with register lengths of 256, is the loop recursive for the cases mentioned?

6. Try compiling the examples in Chapter 4 with your compiler to see how it compares with the Cray compilers used in Chapter 4.

4

VECTORIZATION OF FORTRAN PROGRAMS

In this chapter we will discuss areas where compilers fall short in optimizing Fortran programs and how programmers can restructure their code to assist the compiler in getting the most out of the target "vector" processor. Although we will primarily be using the Cray X-MP with compilers CFT 77 version 1.2 and CFT 1.15BF2, most of the examples used in this chapter are unoptimizable by any of the current compilers. In fact, some of the examples show that the more sophisticated compilers actually generate code that runs more slowly than it would if the code had not been optimized. We hope that these examples will illustrate why the programmer must be involved in optimizing the Fortran program.

4.1
OBTAINING TIMING STATISTICS

In the "real world," a Fortran programmer is faced with the complicated problem of optimizing a very large Fortran application. If the approach to optimization is well organized, the programmer can reduce this complicated task into a number of smaller, manageable pieces of code. Only in the rarest of cases would we need to totally rewrite the Fortran code to optimize it.

Since we will be dividing the task into smaller disjoint steps, it is important to identify the most time-consuming portions of code and then concentrate the optimization on these. A common fault of programmers optimizing a Fortran application is assuming that they know which portions of code use most of the central-processing time and beginning optimization without ever obtaining accurate run-time statistics. This often results from the belief that the distribution of time on a "scalar" computer will carry over to a vector processor. This assumption is usually very inaccurate. Since some of the code will probably vectorize, those code sections will take a lesser percentage of time than they took in scalar execution.

All of the supercomputer manufacturers understand the importance of locating the "hot spots" (the most time-consuming portions of the code). They have supplied tools for assisting their users in instrumenting the code to obtain the information necessary to determine the parts of their programs to optimize first.

4.1.1   Flow Trace

The first such tool, which is extremely easy to use, is FLOW TRACE from Cray Research. A simple switch on the compiler generates run-time statistics, which are then tabulated in a summary after the execution of the program. Figure 4.1 is an example of FLOW TRACE statistics on the LINPACK benchmark from the Argonne National Laboratory.*

Figure 4.1(a) presents the names of the subroutines in alphabetical order. The second column in the figure indicates the amount of time spent in

```
     F L O W  T R A C E   --  Alphabetized summary

          Routine            Time executing  Called  Average T
     10 EPSLON             >>>     (  0.00%)       1       >>> @00000201a Called by        SLINP
      4 ISAMAX           0.065     (  3.56%)    2574         > @00000242a Called by        SGEFA
      2 MATGEN           0.554     ( 30.45%)      27     0.021 @00002552a Called by        SLINP
      6 SAXPY            0.851     ( 46.77%) 133874         > Called by        SGEFA      SGESL
        @00002727a                                                                128700      5174
(a)   3 SGEFA            0.316     ( 17.37%)      26     0.012 @00003642a Called by        SLINP
      7 SGESL            0.013     (  0.71%)      26         > @00004046a Called by        SLINP
      1 SLINP            0.003     (  0.16%)       1     0.003 @00000370a Called by
      9 SMXPY              >       (  0.01%)       1         > @00004324a Called by        SLINP
      5 SSCAL            0.018     (  0.97%)    2574         > @00004766a Called by        SGEFA
      * * * TOTAL        1.820   .  139104 Total calls

     F L O W  T R A C E   --  Calling tree

          1     SLINP       00000370a
          2        MATGEN      00002552a
          3        SGEFA       00003642a
          4           ISAMAX      00000242a
(b)       5           SSCAL       00004766a
          6           SAXPY       00002727a
          7        SGESL       00004046a
          8           SAXPY       00002727a
          9        SMXPY       00004324a
         10     EPSLON      00000201a
```

FIGURE 4.1
FLOW TRACE from LINPACK. (a) Alphabetized summary.
b) Calling tree.

*J. J. Dongarra et al., *LINPACK User's Guide* (Philadelphia: Society of Industrial and Applied Mathematics, 1979).

each routine, with percentage of total time shown in parentheses. The third column is the number of times each routine is called, and the fourth column is the average time per call. A single right-angle bracket ($>$) indicates that the time per call is small, and a pair ($>>$) indicates that the time is extremely small. In the final column, the callers of each routine are listed. If more than one subroutine calls the routine then the number of calls for each caller is given.

Figure 4.1(b) provides the calling tree for executing the program; indentation indicates the branch level within the tree. Given this information, we can now concentrate our optimization within the important routines. A shortcoming of FLOW TRACE is that it only provides timings on subroutine boundaries. Very often, if the subroutine that uses most of the time is very large, we will have difficulty identifying which portions of the large subroutine should be optimized.

On some UNIX systems, a profiler of central processing time can analyze the time used within a subroutine on a line-by-line basis. Another package, called SPY, is available on a number of computers. SPY gives timings internal to each subprogram based on statistical sampling of the program address register of the CPU. Unfortunately, interpreting the results from these other packages is more difficult than those of FLOW TRACE.

4.1.2 FORGE Timing Facility

In our work we have found the need to develop our own timing facility that gives timing statistics on DO loop boundaries, since these are typically where vectorization begins. In addition, information such as DO loop-iteration count (length) and the amount of time spent in a subroutine as a result of each call to that subroutine are tabulated in a summary table after executing the program. Appendix B, Section 1 presents statistics from our timing facility for the LINPACK benchmark.

These statistics contain significantly more information than those in FLOW TRACE. In the first table, information similar to that of FLOW TRACE is given; inclusive and exclusive times and percentages are presented. Inclusive time includes the time spent in all the subroutines and functions called from the routine. Exclusive time excludes the time of called routines if they have also been instrumented. As with FLOW TRACE, if a subroutine or function is not compiled with the timing instrumentation, its time is added to that of its caller.

After this initial table, statistics within each of the subroutines and functions are presented. In these tables, each subroutine and function call as well as every DO loop has an entry. For each DO loop the indentation indicates the nesting of the loop. The next few columns show the time spent in each subprogram or DO loop as a percentage of the total job time or total routine time. Next, the number of times the subprogram or DO statement was executed is given and finally the average and maximum number of iterations for each of the DO loops. At the end of the statistics, the complete calling chain of the program is presented; indentation shows the nesting both of subprograms and DO loops. In this table, the average number of DO loop iterations is shown in brackets ([ ]).

4.1.3   How to Use the Timing Statistics

Obtaining these statistics will result in longer execution, since the calls to the instrumentation routines will take up some time. This additional computer time is well worth the expenditure when this information directs the person hours invested in optimizing the program.

When obtaining timing statistics by execution of the instrumented program, it is important to assure that they represent a typical productive run of the program. Never run a small test case to obtain statistics to be used to direct the optimization of a large test case. In numerical models that march across time in discrete steps, we must time enough (say, four to five) steps to accumulate good averaged statistics; one time step will not suffice.

To completely optimize all important routines in the program, we may have to time several different test cases that exercise all the important pieces of the program. In obtaining the run-time statistics, a good investment in time and analysis will save a lot of misdirected restructuring work later.

Comparing Scalar and Vector Execution of a Program

A good first approach in gathering run-time statistics is to determine how much optimization is already being performed by the compiler. This can be done by making a normal run of the program, allowing the compiler to optimize whatever code sections that it can, and then also obtaining the same statistics from a "scalar" execution of the program. This can be accomplished by turning off vectorization or parallelization. All of the compilers provide a simple mechanism on the control statement to accomplish this. For example, on a Cray with the COS operating system, compile with CFT specifying the keyword OFF = V.

The first advantage of obtaining these results is that we can get a quick idea of the performance to be gained from optimizing this program. If the "normal" execution is the same speed as the "scalar," then no optimization has been performed by the compiler and much stands to be gained. But if the "normal" execution runs from 5 to 6 times faster than the "scalar," then the code is probably already optimized significantly and little can be gained from any more optimization. Most actual results are between these two extremes. After we obtain this global overview of the performance, we need to look at the program subroutine by subroutine. In analyzing the individual subroutines and DO loops, we should concentrate first on those that are most time consuming. Three possibilities exist when we compare vector and scalar times on the subroutine or DO loop level:

1. The vector and scalar executions have identical times. In this case, the compiler has not been able to optimize anything, and we can expect a large performance improvement if restructuring the subroutine or DO loop is possible.

2. The vector time of the routine or DO loop is significantly (a factor of five to ten) less than the scalar. In this case there may not be much that can be done. Section 4.9.6 deals with further optimizing code already optimized by the compiler to some degree.

3. The vector execution of the routine or DO loop is slower than the scalar. Do not be shocked by this possibility. Sometimes the compiler may try to optimize a very complicated section of code and actually generate code that runs more slowly. A simple example of this occurs in the compilation of a doubly nested DO loop with variables specifying the iteration counts (vector lengths). Sometimes the compiler blindly chooses the shorter of the two to optimize, and the vector length turns out to be only one or two at execution time. In these cases we should be able to assist the compiler in doing the right thing by restructuring the code appropriately. Examples such as this will be discussed in section 4.9.7.

Characteristics of Major Routines

Once we identify the routines that use much of the central processing time and have good potential for optimization, we then need to examine the characteristics of the routine and DO loop structure.

1. The most common case occurs when the routine that uses most of the CPU time does not vectorize and contains DO loops of a good size. "Good size" is very machine dependent; but all machines tend to do better on DO loops of 50 or more iterations. When a programmer is faced with such a routine, then the optimization strategy is simply to restructure the DO loops so that they will vectorize. Sections 4.9.1 through 4.9.8 deal with such examples.

2. A more difficult situation occurs when a CPU-intensive subprogram has no DO loops or has DO loops of a very small iteration count (< 10). Since vectorization of loops of such a small size has little payoff, the strategy must be to examine the routines that call this

subprogram to determine if the call is from within a loop with a large iteration count. We can then attempt to vectorize the calling loop. The example shown in Appendix B, Section 2 illustrates such a situation. Subprogram CINVA uses most of the time (in this case 46%), but its DO loops are only of vector length 3. An analysis of the routines that call CINVA shows that RHS, STEP, and FILTRX each call CINVA from DO loops of length 60, an excellent size for vectorization. Section 4.9.9 deals with techniques either to expand subroutines in line or pull DO loops into the routine for subsequent optimization.

3. Sometimes a CPU-intensive routine contains loop nests whose outer loops have much greater iteration counts than do the inner loops. Such loop nests can be restructured to pull the longer loops inside the smaller inner loops. Or, as an alternative, the smaller DO loops can be unrolled inside the larger DO loops. These techniques are discussed in section 4.9.7. Referring to subroutine RHS in Appendix B.2, we see that DO loop 15 within RHS uses most of the time within RHS; but inner loops of length 3 are contained within loop 15.

4.2
DISCUSSION OF AMDAHL'S LAW

The discussion of Amdahl's Law in Chapter 1 addressed the comparison of strictly "scalar" code to "vectorized" code. It is important to understand to what extent the code is already optimized to estimate how much effort is needed to achieve the desired improvement gain. We can apply a cost analysis that compares the amount of effort required with the amount of savings in computer time. If little optimization has been performed to date, then the cost analysis should be favorable for proceeding with an optimization plan. Conversely, if the comparison of the scalar and vector execution times indicates that program has already been significantly optimized, then expending additional effort to achieve more improvement may be unjustifiable. The "law of diminishing returns" applies to program optimization.

An assumption made in deriving Amdahl's law was that vectorization would achieve a factor of ten over scalar code for a Cray X-MP. In fact, sometimes the performance improvement may be greater than or less than ten. The bulk of this chapter is devoted to a great many examples that illustrate the variations in performance. Furthermore, performance gains are a function of vector length. Given the characteristics of a Fortran program and the vector lengths (number of DO loop iterations) involved, the reader can estimate an achievable performance gain for the subroutine to be optimized.

4.3
MODULARITY AND OPTIMIZATION

When developing a sizable program, an excellent approach is to modularize the program and develop the individual modules in such a way that they can be tested independently. Some Fortran programmers have taken modularity to an extreme, and this destroys any possibility of optimization by the compiler.

If a Fortran DO loop references any nonintrinsic subprograms, it cannot be automatically vectorized by a compiler. Often a program with such characteristics has been written so that each subroutine updates single values of its arguments and therefore is a "scalar" subroutine. A far superior approach is to write a subroutine to update arrays of values. In this case the DO loops are contained within the routines and are more likely to be optimized by the compiler.

4.3.1 Scalar-Valued Routines versus Array-Valued Routines

Consider a routine that calculates some complicated physical quantity for a particle. In loop 40000, subroutine COMPL is called on each iteration to use the scalar variables X, Y, and Z.

```
      DO 40000 I = 1, N
        CALL COMPL(X,Y,Z)
40000 CONTINUE

      SUBROUTINE COMPL(X,Y,Z)
        . . .
      X = ...
      (Complicated calculations using scalar quantities)
        = ... Y ...
        = ... X ... Z ...
        . . .
      RETURN
      END
```

A far superior approach places the loop inside COMPL, which then receives and returns arrays of values from and to its calling routine, performing the computation within a potentially vectorizable DO loop.

```
      CALL COMPL(N,X,Y,Z)

      SUBROUTINE COMPL(N,X,Y,Z)
      DIMENSION X(*),Y(*),Z(*)
      DO 40001 I = 1,N
        . . .
      X(I) = ...
```

```
           (Complicated calculations using array quantities)
              = ... Y(I) ...
              = ... X(I) ... Z(I) ...
                 ...
40001 CONTINUE
       RETURN
       END
```

Note that COMPL could be called (albeit inefficiently) with N = 1 to perform the same calculations as the original version of COMPL.

The guideline to use when restructuring code or developing code from scratch is to make array operations visible to the compiler. If the DO loops are in the calling routines and the CPU-intensive calculations are contained within the subroutines or functions called from the DO loop, the compiler is blind to the fact that there are good calculations that could be vectorized on the DO loop.

4.4
A SYSTEMATIC APPROACH TO RESTRUCTURING

Once the most time-consuming portions of the program are identified, the programmer should optimize systematically. We should not try to optimize the entire program prior to testing intermediate restructurings for accuracy and performance gains. By setting up a test case that executes relatively quickly, we can submit a test after a major DO loop or small routine has been optimized. Both correctness of results and the performance gain should be examined. Sometimes a restructuring may not achieve the desired goal, and an alternative approach may be warranted. If two subroutines are being optimized, one using 70% of the time and the other 20%, and only a factor-of-two performance gain is obtained on the first routine, it is still using more time than the second routine and should be examined for additional improvements.

The best approach for vectorizing a large Fortran program is to restructure a small amount of code (perhaps three or four hours of work), test it for accuracy and performance, then go on to a second piece of code.

4.4.1   Possible Inaccuracies Caused by Vectorization

When restructuring a program for vectorization, it is most important to continue to obtain correct results. Some optimization techniques can cause slight differences in the answers. The best example of this is the vectorization of a summation. When a summation is vectorized, the result is often computed in a different order than that performed in scalar mode. For instance, consider the example in loop 40010.

```
      SUM = 0.0
      DO 40010 I = 1, 1001
      SUM = SUM + A(I)
40010 CONTINUE
```

The reason for the difference in the order of calculations in vector mode is that the compiler generates code that will calculate partial sums in vector registers, then adds the partial sums together. In scalar mode, SUM is generated by adding the elements of A in order. Consider the following values for the elements of A:

```
A( 1 : 1000  ) = 1.E-15

 A( 1001) = 1.
```

If we accumulate these values in scalar mode on a machine that has 15 decimal digits of accuracy, we will obtain the result 1.00000000000100. But if the values are added in reverse order (this is not the way it is done in vector mode), the result will be 1.0 because of roundoff on each add operation; that is, on a machine with 15 digits of accuracy, $1.0 + 1.E-15 = 1.0$.

Differences in the summation resulting from vector versus scalar are typically very small and are encountered rarely. For arithmetic operations that are not accumulative, the results will be identical whether obtained by vector or scalar execution.

4.5
WHY THE PROGRAMMER IS NEEDED

The techniques discussed in this chapter for optimizing code are not very complicated. As a matter of fact, most vectorizing compilers today perform all of the techniques outlined here. But, compilers are very often inhibited from performing these techniques because their analysis is blocked by the structure of the Fortran code, and they cannot determine if the techniques can be safely applied.

A programmer can write Fortran code that defies analysis by any compiler. For example, sophisticated equivalencing among variables and arrays will hinder compilers from doing good data-dependency analysis. Tricks that some programmers use to take some short-cuts in writing the code may result in poorly executing scalar code and will often prevent vectorization.

The intent of this chapter is to discuss the optimization techniques that many compilers perform and conditions in which the compilers cannot employ these techniques. In many of these cases a programmer can use the methods described in this chapter to restructure the code so that the compiler will optimize the new version.

4.5.1 Difficulties of Optimizing "Dusty-Deck" Fortran

In analyzing Fortran programs, a compiler will often encounter "inhibitors," which are constructs within a DO loop that degrade or prevent vectorization. Ambiguous conditions also cause the compiler to make an arbitrary choice of how to vectorize the code. Frequently, compilers use other characteristics of the loop—such as the order of subscripts in multidimensioned arrays—to try to determine how to optimize the code; sometimes inefficient code results from a bad choice. We will examine both of these situations in the subsections that follow.

4.6 CANDIDATES FOR VECTORIZATION

In Chapter 3 we established a vocabulary for discussing the important constructs of a DO loop. Now we can begin to define what will and will not implicitly vectorize. All of the compilers on supercomputers investigate inner DO loops to determine if they contain either or both of the following:

- A store into at least one array with a loop variant subscript expression (a vector array)
- At least one recognized reduction function

An inner loop that contains one of the preceding is a candidate for vectorization. But before any vector instructions can be generated, the loop must be examined for vectorization inhibitors, as we will outline next.

4.7 VECTORIZATION INHIBITORS

If a loop contains any of the following constructs, part or all of the loop may not vectorize:

1. Recursion in any of its forms: fetching and storing of the same array with subscript expressions that will or might cause data feedback from one iteration of the loop to a subsequent iteration; fetching a scalar or array constant prior to setting it in the loop

2. Subroutine CALLs

3. References to external functions for which the compiler knows of no vector version. Most Fortran 77 intrinsic functions such as SQRT, SIN, EXP, and so forth are vectorized; user-defined functions are not.

4. Any I/O statements

5. Assigned GO TO statements

6. Certain nested IF blocks. The payoff for vectorization decreases as the level of nesting increases.

7. GO TO statements that exit the loop. Some compilers have a limited ability to vectorize this in simple loops, but in general such loops are run in scalar mode.

8. Backward transfers within a loop

All of the compilers will tell us which loops have been vectorized. Most of them will tell us what vectorization inhibitors appear in a loop and what parts of the loop will be run in scalar mode. If a compiler does not tell us why a loop does not vectorize, close examination of the loop will almost certainly reveal one of the preceding inhibitors. If no inhibitors can be found, the loop is probably too long for effective optimization/vectorization, a condition that can be remedied by splitting the loop using techniques outlined in subsequent sections.

For completeness, it must be noted that some of the compilers will examine all of the loops in a nest in an attempt to determine on which to vectorize. If an outer loop is chosen, the loop nest will be transparently inverted to make the target loop the inner loop. Such "loop switching" is the subject of a later section. Some of the compilers will also "collapse" loop nests when the subscripts of the referenced arrays range over all possible array elements, as in loop 40020.

```
        DIMENSION A(90,50), B(90,50)
              . . .
        DO 40020 J = 1, 50
           DO 40020 I = 1,90
              A(I,J) = B(I,J) * 2.0
40020 CONTINUE
```

Later we will examine each problem area in detail, specifying techniques that will allow as much code as possible to be vectorized. In most cases we will keep the example loops and their restructuring as simple as possible. Real-world code can be expected to realize even better performance gains than illustrated here.

4.7.1   Compiler Optimization with Incomplete Information

Some of today's compilers appear to be less sophisticated than others. This is because some compiler writers have taken the approach that if they really do not know the best way to optimize a particular loop, they will not optimize it at all, because it may produce slower code. Others have chosen to take a "best guess" to optimize complicated loops. Following are some typical conditions in which a compiler lacks enough information about the code to optimize effectively:

1. Multinested DO loops. The Cray compilers currently are vectorizing only the innermost DO loop. This may not be a bad approach, since the results from compilers that attempt to switch loop nests indicate that the heuristics determining which is the best loop to vectorize improve performance only about 50% of the time.

2. Complex decision processes. All compilers have a limit on the level of nesting of IF conditions that they will attempt to vectorize. The nesting of the IFs is some indication of the sparsity of the truth of the compounded conditions (and therefore the effective vector length). But it certainly is not always the best means of determining whether the condition should be vectorized or not.

3. Ambiguous array subscripts. When the relation among differing subscripts in references to the same array within a loop cannot be determined, a compiler must be concerned about the potential data dependency of the calculations. Some compilers handle such ambiguities by generating two versions of the DO loop: a vector version to be used if a run-time test indicates that the subscripts do not lead to recursion and a scalar version to be used otherwise. But, only a few such ambiguities in a loop can be handled effectively in this manner.

Often, compilers are inhibited from doing the best optimization because they do not know enough about the code. The solution is to involve the programmer in the analysis. Even a programmer does not know all of the answers needed for optimization; but, if assisted by run-time statistics, he or she can usually provide the necessary information.

The authors believe that it will be a significant time before a compiler can automatically optimize the dusty-deck Fortran program well. So, for today, the right approach is for the programmer to become involved in the analysis, aided by run-time statistics.

4.8
EFFECTS OF ARRAY ACCESS ON PERFORMANCE

Before examining restructuring techniques on actual loops, we wish to establish the effect on performance, depending on the order in which the elements of arrays are fetched and stored, and furthermore, on the ratio of operations to vector operands within a loop.

To this end, we have prepared three groups of loops. The first accesses arrays indirectly with random indexes. The second accesses the same arrays directly with unitary stride; and the third accesses the arrays directly with stride 128. Each group contains 13 different loops. And, from group to group, corresponding loops perform the same number of operations on the same number of vectors. Each vector fetched or stored within a loop is counted as an operand, and within a group the ratio of operations to operands ranges from as small as one-third (one operation, three operands) to as large as nine and one-half (nineteen operations, two operands).

We expect that unitary stride will produce the best performance among the three groups. Indirect addressing adds one or more chimes to the execution. This occurs because of the extra time needed to fetch the index and also because of general memory performance degradation resulting from interference among the indexes and the requirement that the indexed array elements be delivered in the proper order. Finally, stride 128 forces memory-bank conflicts on each successive reference and slows the performance by a factor equal to the memory-bank cycle time. (Since there are 39 loops involved in this comparison, we have listed them in Appendix C.)

We have run all the loops on the Cray X-MP (with G/S, CFT 77), the CYBER 205 (with FTN 200) and the NEC SX2 and computed the performance in megaflops for each. The results, comparing the three modes of memory accessing, are graphed versus the ratio of operations to operands in Figure 4.2.

As the ratio of operations to operands increases, the performance of the target machines approaches the maximum possible. For example, on the Cray X-MP the examples with larger ratios are generating an add and multiply each clock cycle most of the time, and the Mflop rate will exceed 200 for very long vector lengths.

The results obtained from these figures are consistent with our assumptions. The contiguous addressing is in fact the fastest of the three methods for all ratios of operations to operands; indirect addressing is second, and a stride of 128 is the slowest. On the Cray X-MP the differences between contiguous and indirect addressing vary from a factor of 2 for low ratios to 1.2 for very high ratios. The higher the ratio, the less time spent in fetching and storing operands and results. The stride 128 results range from a factor of three to less than a factor of two.

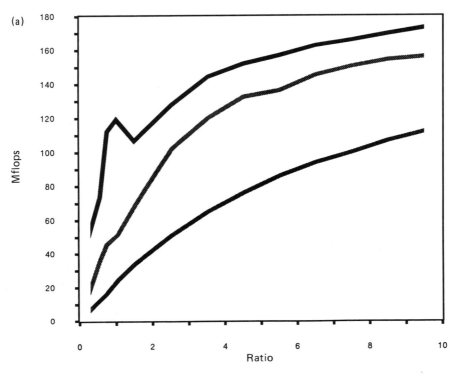

(a)

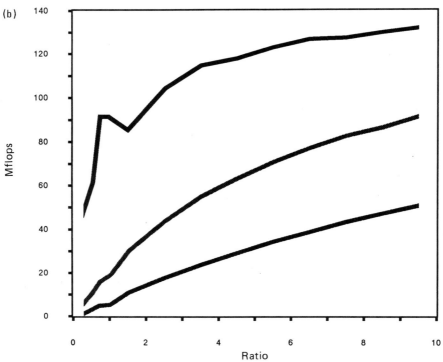

(b)

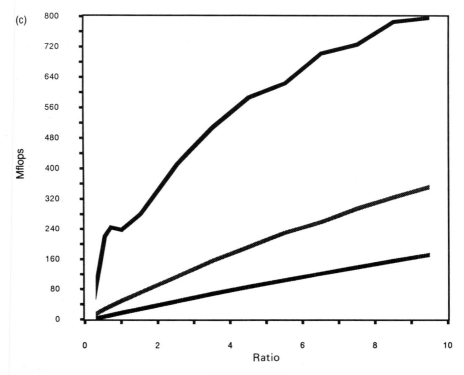

FIGURE 4.2
Performance versus Ratio of Operations to Operands. (a) Cray
X-MP. (b) CYBER 205. (c) NEC SX2. Loops: contiguous,
top line; indirect, middle line; stride = 128, bottom line.

On the CYBER 205 the differences are significantly larger. The difference between indirect and contiguous addressing ranges from factors of 5 to 6 down to a factor of 1.5.

```
C       ONE OPERATION - THREE OPERANDS      RATIO = 1/3
        DO 41000 I = 1, N
          A(IA(I)) = B(IA(I)) + C(IA(I))
41000 CONTINUE

C       ONE OPERATION - THREE OPERANDS      RATIO = 1/3
        DO 41020 I = 1, N
          A(I) = B(I) + C(I)
41020 CONTINUE
```

Let us examine the performance of the Cyber 205 in more detail. Considering DO loop 41000 and DO loop 41020, the operations needed to perform loop 41000 are as follows:

• Gather B(IA(I)) into a temporary memory vector TEMP1.
• Gather C(IA(I)) into a temporary memory vector TEMP2.

- Add TEMP1 to TEMP2 storing results into temporary memory vector TEMP3.

- Scatter TEMP3 into A(IA(I)).

In loop 41020 none of the temporary vectors are needed. If all these operations took the same amount of time, we would expect loop 41020 to run four times faster than loop 41000. In fact the gather/scatter operations take more time than the add operation. Therefore, the results differ by more than a factor of four.

The memory architecture of the CYBER 205 and ETA 10 causes fetching and storing of arrays with nonunitary strides to be treated almost identical to indirect addressing. This is because the arrays must be fetched into temporary vectors with gather-periodic instructions and the result stored into an array with a scatter-periodic instruction. These periodic operations take about the same time as the indirect address gather/scatter and result in approximately the same timings. The results in this example for nonunitary stride have the added difficulty of encountering memory-bank conflicts.

The results on the NEC SX2 vector processor are very interesting. We know less about the actual fetching and storing of arrays on this machine, but our example gives us some insight on its relative performance. The first point is that the SX2 is a very fast machine, capable of reaching almost 800 Mflops on the highest ratio with unitary stride fetching and storing. The second point is that indirect fetching and storing is significantly slower than unitary strides. The contiguous accessing is three to four times faster than the Cray X-MP, but its indirect addressing is about the same speed as the Cray X-MP for small ratios and only a factor of two for larger ratios. The SX2 does have hardware gather/scatter, but its result rate is only about one-fourth to one-third of its contiguous performance. Finally, note that stride 128 performance is about one-eighth that of contiguous vectors, indicating that the bank cycle time is eight clock cycles.

4.9
EXAMPLES OF RESTRUCTURING FORTRAN LOOPS

4.9.1 Introduction to Examples

For the remainder of this chapter we will examine a set of typical Fortran loops, highlighting constructs within each loop that can degrade or prevent compiler optimization. A restructuring of each loop is presented, and the performance of the original and the restructured loops are compared graphically.

Most of the loops are drawn from real-world programs or well-known benchmarks. A few have been fabricated to present a particular problem with a short example. We have attempted to represent all of the commonly encountered problem areas and to present effective restructuring techniques that will work well on any vector processor.

All of the loop comparisons have been made on a Cray X-MP/48 (at the Pittsburgh Supercomputing Center), using either CFT 77 ver. 1.2 or CFT 1.15BF2. Some examples are shown for the CDC CYBER 205 at the Minnesota Supercomputer Center.

4.9.2   Accessing Arrays

The following example simply illustrates the effect of memory-bank conflicts on the Cray X-MP. In loop 41080 we are accessing the arrays on the second subscript of the A array. Since the first dimension is 128, this is the stride through memory, which we know causes memory-bank conflicts. When this situation arises, a common restructuring technique is to change the offending dimension to a value that will not cause a memory-bank conflict. In loop 41081 we have changed the dimension to 129, and the resultant odd stride does not encounter memory-bank conflicts. We can see in Figure 4.3 that the

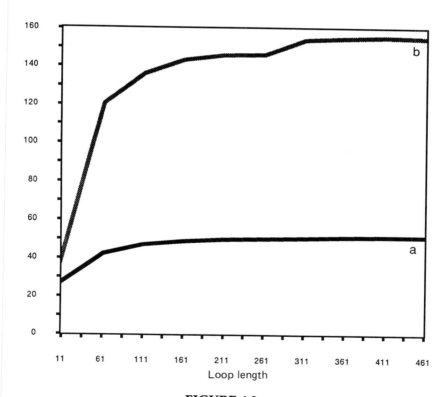

FIGURE 4.3

Performance Comparison of Loops 41080 and 41081, Cray X-MP. a, original; b, restructured.

restructured code (dotted line) runs up to three times faster than the original
code (solid line).

```
DIMENSION A(128,N)
       ...
DO 41080  I = 1,N
  A( 1,I) = C1*A(13,I) + C2* A(12,I) + C3*A(11,I) +
*             C4*A(10,I) + C5* A( 9,I) + C6*A( 8,I) +
*             C7*A( 7,I) + C0*(A( 5,I) + A( 6,I) )  + A( 3,I)
41080 CONTINUE

DIMENSION A(129,N)
       ...
DO 41081 I = 1,N
  A( 1,I) = C1*A(13,I) + C2* A(12,I) + C3*A(11,I) +
*             C4*A(10,I) + C5* A( 9,I) + C6*A( 8,I) +
*             C7*A( 7,I) + C0*(A( 5,I) + A( 6,I) )  + A( 3,I)
41081 CONTINUE
```

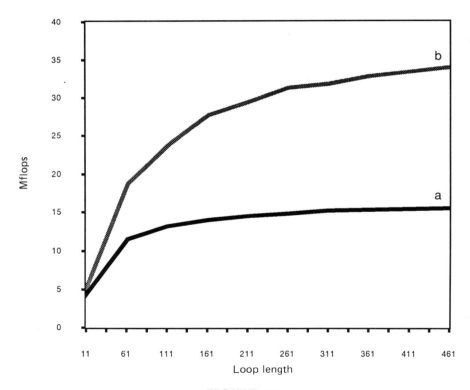

FIGURE 4.4
Performance Comparison of Loops 41080 and 41081, CYBER
205. a, original; b, restructured.

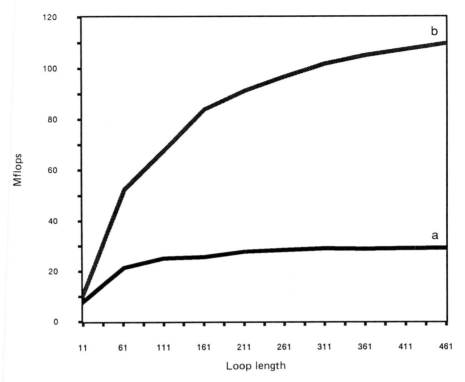

FIGURE 4.5
Performance Comparison of Loops 41090 and 41091, Cray
X-MP. a, original; b, restructured.

On the Cyber 205 the results are better in the restructured code shown in Figure 4.4. But the most effective restructuring would be somehow to switch dimensions of the array. In that way the I index would be the innermost, and the accessing of arrays would be contiguous. That restructuring was not performed here because of the impact it would have on the remaining code in the program. In fact, in other portions of the program the array may be accessed on the first subscript. If the subscripts were reversed, then the accessing would again be noncontiguous and again run more slowly.

The next example shows such a restructuring that will undoubtedly help the Cyber 205 significantly. In loop 41090 the innermost loop on I is accessing the arrays on the third subscript. The stride is therefore the product of the first two dimensions of the arrays, or 64. Our restructuring in loop 41091 is to rearrange the order and meaning of the dimensions and subscripts to have the inner loop access the left-most subscript and largest vector length. The results are depicted in Figure 4.5.

```
C       THE ORIGINAL
        DIMENSION A(8,8,500,8), B(8,8,500,8)
                ...
        DO 41090 K = KA, KE, -1
          DO 41090 J = JA, JE
            DO 41090 I = IA, IE
              A(K,L,I,J) = A(K,L,I,J) - B(J,1,I,K)*A(K+1,L,I,1)
     *        - B(J,2,I,K)*A(K+1,L,I,2) - B(J,3,I,K)*A(K+1,L,I,3)
     *        - B(J,4,I,K)*A(K+1,L,I,4) - B(J,5,I,K)*A(K+1,L,I,5)
41090 CONTINUE

C       THE RESTRUCTURED
        DIMENSION A(500,8,8,8), B(500,8,8,8)
                ...
        DO 41091 K = KA, KE, -1
          DO 41091 J = JA, JE
            DO 41091 I = IA, IE
              A(I,K,L,J) = A(I,K,L,J) - B(I,J,1,K)*A(I,K+1,L,1)
     *        - B(I,J,2,K)*A(I,K+1,L,2) - B(I,J,3,K)*A(I,K+1,L,3)
     *        - B(I,J,4,K)*A(I,K+1,L,4) - B(I,J,5,K)*A(I,K+1,L,5)
41091 CONTINUE
```

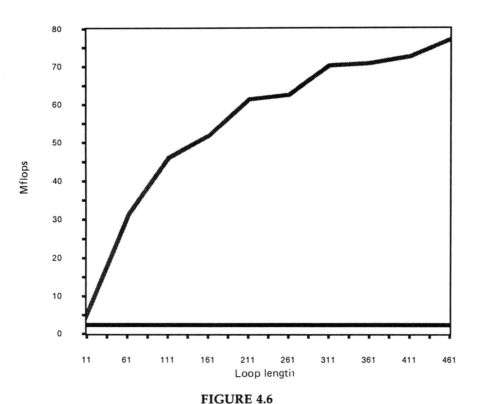

FIGURE 4.6

Performance Comparison of Loops 41090 and 41091, CYBER 205. Original, solid line; restructured, dotted line.

If we assume that the dimensions of the arrays can be switched as shown so that accessing can be contiguous, the results on all the machines are favorable—but most favorable on the Cyber 205. These results are depicted in Figure 4.6.

4.9.3   Scalar Temporaries (Simple)

Recall that a scalar temporary is a scalar variable set equal to a vectorizable expression within a loop. Often, we will encounter a program in which scalar temporaries have been used to such an extent that the ability of the compiler to optimize the loop is compromised. Loop 42010 represents such a case. Notice that 12 scalar temporaries are assigned before the compiler can use any of them. Unless the compiler is very smart and can reorganize the statements, it will run out of registers (there are only eight vector registers on the Crays).

Loop 42011 generates the same results with no scalar temporaries. Notice the grouping, in parentheses, of the common subexpressions. Both the original and the restructured loops vectorize; but for vector lengths over 100, loop 42011 outperforms 42010 by a factor of 1.8 (Figure 4.7).

Later sections will explore the restructuring of more complicated use of scalars in a loop.

```
C         THE ORIGINAL
          DO 42010 KK = 1, N
          T000        = A(KK,K000)
          T001        = A(KK,K001)
          T010        = A(KK,K010)
          T011        = A(KK,K011)
          T100        = A(KK,K100)
          T101        = A(KK,K101)
          T110        = A(KK,K110)
          T111        = A(KK,K111)
          B1          = B(KK,K000)
          B2          = B(KK,K001)
          B3          = B(KK,K010)
          B4          = B(KK,K011)
          R1          = T100 * C1 + T110 * C2
          S1          = T101 * C1 - T111 * C2
          RS          = T000 + R1
          SS          = T001 + S1
          RU          = T010 - R1
          SU          = T011 - S1
          B(KK,K000)  = B1 + RS
          B(KK,K001)  = B2 + RU
          B(KK,K010)  = B3 + SS
          B(KK,K011)  = B4 - SU
42010 CONTINUE

C         THE RESTRUCTURED
          DO 42011 KK = 1,N
          B(KK,K000)  = B(KK,K000)        + A(KK,K000)
        *               + (A(KK,K100) * C1 + A(KK,K110) * C2)
```

```
      B(KK,K001)  = B(KK,K001)            + A(KK,K010)
   *                - (A(KK,K100) * C1 + A(KK,K110) * C2)
      B(KK,K010)  = B(KK,K010)            + A(KK,K001)
   *                + (A(KK,K101) * C1 - A(KK,K111) * C2)
      B(KK,K011)  = B(KK,K011)            - A(KK,K011)
   *                + (A(KK,K101) * C1 - A(KK,K111) * C2)
42011 CONTINUE
```

When used moderately in a loop, scalar temporaries are very useful for helping a compiler to recognize common subexpressions. Loop 42030 is loop 10 of the Livermore kernels, and it is vectorized by all compilers.* We might think that additional optimization could be obtained by eliminating some of the scalar temporaries. This turns out to be incorrect, since—after applying

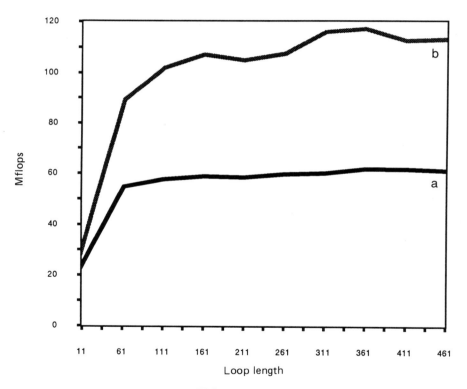

FIGURE 4.7
Performance Comparison of Loops 42010 and 42011, Cray
X-MP. a, original; b, restructured.

* Frank H. McMahon, "The Livermore Fortran Kernels: A Computer Test of the Numerical Performance Range," Lawrence Livermore National Laboratory, University of California—Berkeley, December 1986.

the same technique used to optimize loop 42011—the restructured loop 42031 actually runs more slowly than the original (Figure 4.8).

The restructuring does illustrate more clearly what is going on in this loop. The calculation of A(14,I) uses old values of A(5,I) through A(13,I). This was done in the original with the use of the scalar temporaries. In eliminating the scalar temporaries, the assignments into the array elements had to be done in reverse order to preserve the correct algorithm. This is an example where the scalar temporaries in the original were useful in minimizing the work the compiler generated.

```
C       THE ORIGINAL
        DO 42030   I = 1, N
        AR      =         B(5,I)
        BR      = AR - A(5,I)
        A(5,I)  = AR
        CR      = BR - A(6,I)
        A(6,I)  = BR
        AR      = CR - A(7,I)
        A(7,I)  = CR
        BR      = AR - A(8,I)
        A(8,I)  = AR
        CR      = BR - A(9,I)
        A(9,I)  = BR
        AR      = CR - A(10,I)
        A(10,I) = CR
        BR      = AR - A(11,I)
        A(11,I) = AR
        CR      = BR - A(12,I)
        A(12,I) = BR
        A(14,I) = CR - A(13,I)
        A(13,I) = CR
42030 CONTINUE


C       THE RESTRUCTURED
        DO 42031   I = 1, N
        A(14,I) =  B(5,I) - A( 5,I) - A( 6,I) - A( 7,I) - A( 8,I)
     *           - A(9,I) - A(10,I) - A(11,I) - A(12,I) - A(13,I)
        A(13,I) =  B(5,I) - A( 5,I) - A( 6,I) - A( 7,I) - A( 8,I)
     *           - A(9,I) - A(10,I) - A(11,I) - A(12,I)
        A(12,I) =  B(5,I) - A( 5,I) - A( 6,I) - A( 7,I) - A( 8,I)
     *           - A(9,I) - A(10,I) - A(11,I)
        A(11,I) =  B(5,I) - A( 5,I) - A( 6,I) - A( 7,I) - A( 8,I)
     *           - A(9,I) - A(10,I)
        A(10,I) =  B(5,I) - A( 5,I) - A( 6,I) - A( 7,I) - A( 8,I)
     *           - A(9,I)
        A(9,I)  =  B(5,I) - A( 5,I) - A( 6,I) - A( 7,I) - A( 8,I)
        A(8,I)  =  B(5,I) - A( 5,I) - A( 6,I) - A( 7,I)
        A(7,I)  =  B(5,I) - A( 5,I) - A( 6,I)
        A(6,I)  =  B(5,I) - A( 5,I)
        A(5,I)  =  B(5,I)
42031 CONTINUE
```

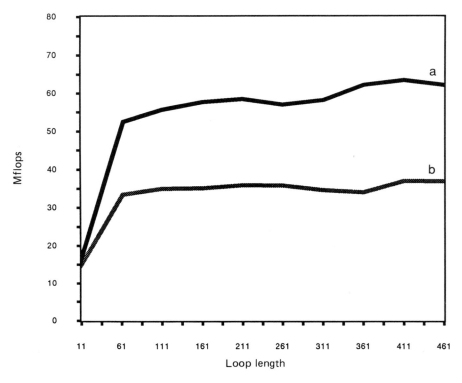

FIGURE 4.8
Performance Comparison of Loops 42030 and 42031, Cray
X-MP. a, original; b, restructured.

4.9.4 Recursion Involving Arrays

In this section we investigate various constructs that often degrade or prevent optimization because of actual or potential recursion in array references. The first example, loop 43010, is not recursive. We present it here to compare the performance of a fully vectorized loop with the recursive loop 43011 that follows.

```
C       NON-RECURSIVE DO LOOP FOR TIMING COMPARISON
        DO 43010 I = 2, N
          A(I) = A(I+1) * B(I) + C(I)
43010 CONTINUE

C         THE ORIGINAL RECURSIVE DO LOOP
        DO 43011 I = 2, N
          A(I) = A(I-1) * B(I) + C(I)
43011 CONTINUE
```

Although no vector instructions can be issued in computing loop 43011, the Cray compiler (as well as most others) recognizes the loop as a special case for which it has a highly optimized scalar solution. The solution is embodied in a library routine FOLR (first order linear recurrence) that the compiler invokes to provide the desired answers. The technique involves the simultaneous computation of several of the loop iterations, thus utilizing all of the machine's scalar registers and scalar memory bandwidth. A close approximation of this technique is shown in standard Fortran in loops 43012 and 43013.

```
C       THE RECURSIVE LOOP UNROLLED TO DEPTH FOUR
        DO 43012 I = 2, N-3, 4
        A(I)    = A(I-1) * B(I)   + C(I)
        A(I+1) = A(I)    * B(I+1) + C(I+1)
        A(I+2) = A(I+1) * B(I+2) + C(I+2)
        A(I+3) = A(I+2) * B(I+3) + C(I+3)
43012 CONTINUE

C         CLEANUP LOOP FOR DEPTH FOUR UNROLLING
        DO 43013 J = I,N
        A(J) = A(J-1) * B(J) + C(J)
43013 CONTINUE
```

This technique of loop unrolling is introduced here in this example where it is relatively easy to follow. It provides no performance improvement over the optimization of the original loop (Figure 4.9). But it will be shown to be a valuable technique in later examples.

The point of loop unrolling is to give the compiler more work to perform on each iteration of the loop. In this case we write out (unroll) four sequential iterations of the original loop and cause the original loop index to increment by four. The number of iterations to unroll is very machine and loop dependent and must usually be determined experimentally. Four is a good number with which to start. Then try three and five, compare performances, and if four is not maximal, try some other depths of unrolling.

Note that for the general case of variable loop length LL and unrolling depth UD, the unrolled loop is complete only if LL mod UD = 0. For an unrolling depth of four, there can be 0, 1, 2, or 3 iterations left to do after the main loop is complete. This is the function of the cleanup loop 43013. Here we take advantage of the ANSI 77 Fortran requirement that upon normal loop termination the DO loop index will have a value equal to its value on the last iteration plus the loop increment. This means that when loop 43012 terminates, I will have one of the values N−2, N−1, N, or N+1. This allows loop 43013 to perform 3, 2, 1, or 0 iterations, as required.

In the next few examples we will examine cases where the compiler may not know if a loop is recursive. Loop nest 42030 is a traditionally coded Gaussian elimination scheme. Most compilers will try to vectorize the inner loop where row subtraction is taking place. Note that A(J,K) is a function of A(J,I). Although both J and I are fixed values within that inner loop, a

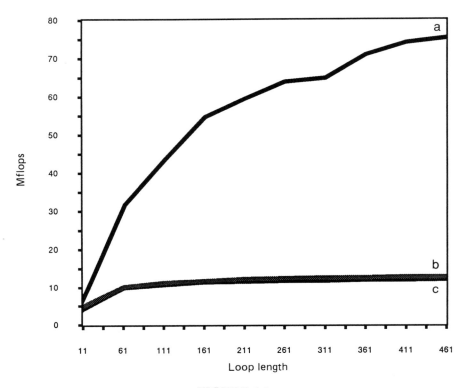

FIGURE 4.9
Performance Comparison of Loops 43010, 43011, 43012, Cray
X-MP. a, 43010; b, FOLR; c, unrolled.

compiler must attempt to determine whether K ever assumes the value of I
(on other than the last iteration), since this would be recursive and must not
be vectorized.

There are two approaches for the compiler in optimizing this case. The
first approach is to be smart enough to recognize that there is no possibility
for recursion, since the initial (and lowest) value of K is I+1. The other
approach is to generate one code sequence for executing the loop in scalar
mode and another sequence to execute it in vector mode, then test at run time
whether K will assume the value of I in the inner loop. This second approach
is called conditional compilation and is used quite extensively by CFT 1.15.

To assure that the compiler does fully vectorize the restructured loop
42031 we have inserted directives (for Alliant, Cray, and NEC in this case)
that inform the compiler to ignore potential recursion within the loop. Figure
4.10 illustrates that performance improves by 50–100% for longer vector
lengths. The performance gain results from the elimination of the execution
time test by the compiler.

```
C     THE ORIGINAL
C   GAUSS ELIMINATION
      DO 43020 I = 1, MATDIM
       A(I,I) = 1. / A(I,I)
       DO 43020 J = I+1, MATDIM
        A(J,I) = A(J,I) * A(I,I)
        DO 43020 K = I+1, MATDIM
         A(J,K) = A(J,K) - A(J,I) * A(I,K)
43020 CONTINUE


C     THE RESTRUCTURED
C   GAUSS ELIMINATION
      DO 43021 I = 1, MATDIM
       A(I,I) = 1. / A(I,I)
       DO 43021 J = I+1, MATDIM
        A(J,I) = A(J,I) * A(I,I)
CVD$ NODEPCHK
CDIR$ IVDEP
*VDIR NODEP
        DO 43021 K = I+1, MATDIM
         A(J,K) = A(J,K) - A(J,I) * A(I,K)
43021 CONTINUE
```

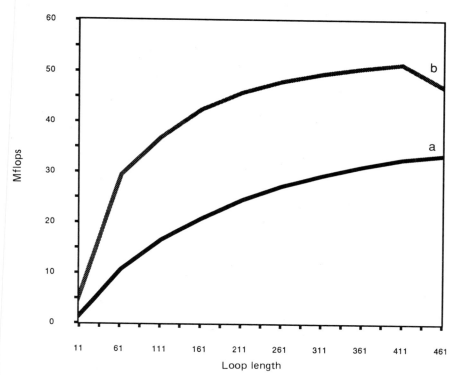

FIGURE 4.10

Performance Comparison of Loops 43020 and 43021, Cray
X-MP. a, original; b, restructured.

A similar problem exists in loop 43030 where the compiler must be concerned about the potential recursion between A(I) and A(I−K). Figure 4.11 illustrates that, although the compiler vectorized the original, the directives improved performance by about 30%.

```
C       THE ORIGINAL
        DO   43030  I = 2, N
         DO   43030  K = 1, I-1
          A(I)= A(I)  + B(I,K) * A(I-K)
43030 CONTINUE


C       THE RESTRUCTURED
        DO 43031 I = 2, N
CVD$ NODEPCHK
CDIR$ IVDEP
*VDIR NODEP
        DO 43031 K = 1, I-1
         A(I) = A(I)  + B(I,K) * A(I-K)
43031 CONTINUE
```

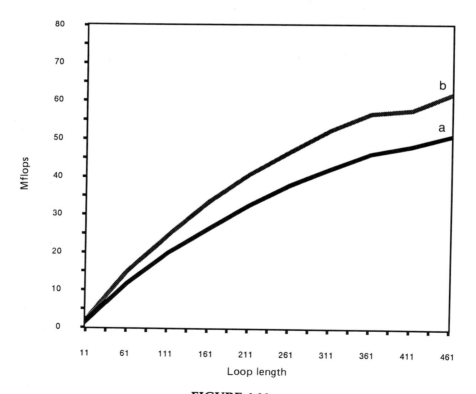

FIGURE 4.11

Performance Comparison of Loops 43030 and 43031, Cray X-MP. a, original; b, restructured.

Any time the same array is indirectly addressed on both sides of an assignment statement, as in loop 43070, a compiler must assume that values will repeat in the index vector, causing the loop to be recursive. In many sparse matrix procedures, the values in the index vector never repeat. If we know that, then we can inform the compiler with a directive — as we have done just before loop 43071. The performance improvement for long vectors approaches a factor of ten over the original (Figure 4.12).

```
C        THE ORIGINAL
         DO 43070 I = 1, N
            A(IA(I)) = A(IA(I)) + CO * B(I)
43070 CONTINUE

C        THE RESTRUCTURED
CDIR$ IVDEP
CVD$  NODEPCHK
*VDIR NODEP
         DO 43071 I = 1, N
            A(IA(I)) = A(IA(I)) + CO * B(I)
43071 CONTINUE
```

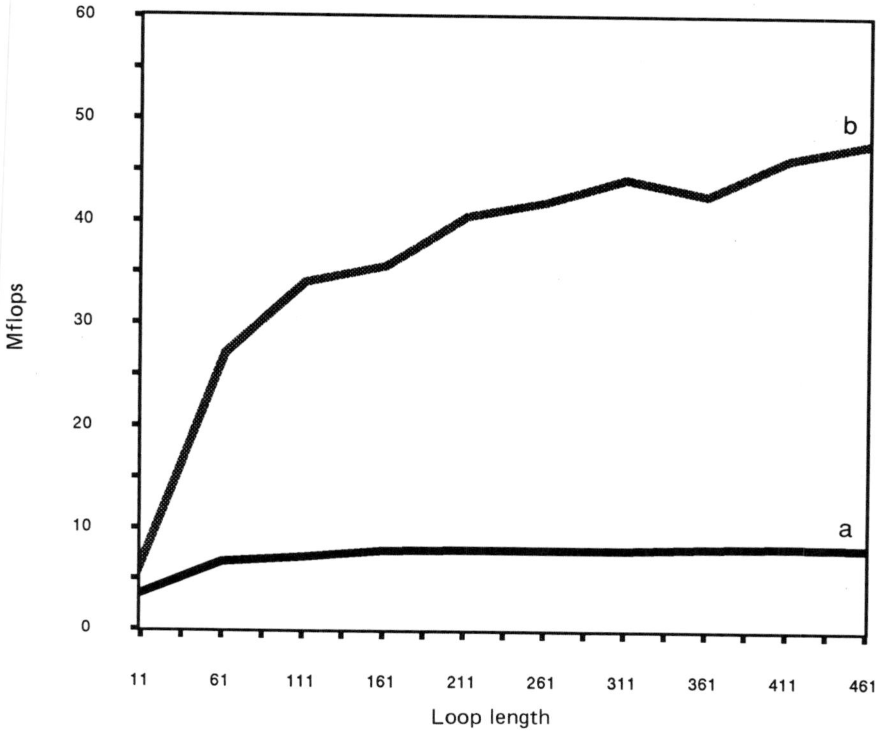

FIGURE 4.12
Performance Comparison of Loops 43070 and 43071, Cray X-MP. a, original; b, restructured.

Next, we have loop 43080 (Livermore kernel 13*), which spends most of its time computing the indirect address indexes I2 and J2 to be used as subscripts in the array A in the last line of the loop. Again, the compiler must guard against the possibility of repeated subscripts and so generates scalar rather than vector instructions. With the MOD2N function involved in the computation, recursion is highly likely; so this is a wise choice.

Whenever we have a partially recursive loop, we should split out the nonrecursive (vectorizable) calculations from the recursive (nonvectorizable) calculations.

Careful inspection of the rest of the loop reveals that all other operations could be vectorized, so we split the loop into two loops, 43081 and 43082, the first of which now vectorizes. To effect this split we must propagate the values of I2 and J2 from the first loop to the second. This is accomplished by introducing the arrays I2V and J2V.

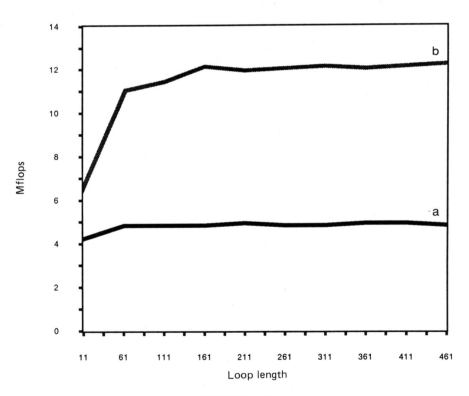

FIGURE 4.13
Performance Comparison of Loops 43080 and 43081, Cray X-MP. a, original; b, restructured.

* Ibid.

Figure 4.13 demonstrates a 100% performance improvement of the restructured over the original loop. Incidentally, the low Mflop numbers illustrate a shortcoming of characterizing loop efficiency in terms of megaflops. In this case the purpose of the loop involves much necessary data motion and relatively few arithmetic operations.

```
C         THE ORIGINAL
C         Statement function MOD2N
          MOD2N (I,J) = AND (I,J-1)
          DO 43080  I = 1, N
              I1 = D(1,I)
              J1 = D(2,I)
              I1 =          1 + MOD2N(I1,64)
              J1 =          1 + MOD2N(J1,64)
          D(3,I) = D(3,I)    + B(I1,J1)
          D(4,I) = D(4,I)    + C(I1,J1)
          D(1,I) = D(1,I)    + D(3,I)
          D(2,I) = D(2,I)    + D(4,I)
              I2 = D(1,I)
              J2 = D(2,I)
              I2 =              MOD2N(I2,64)
              J2 =              MOD2N(J2,64)
          D(1,I) = D(1,I)    + G(J2+32)
          D(2,I) = D(2,I)    + H(J2+32)
              I2 = I2        + E(I2+32)
              J2 = J2        + F(J2+32)
          A(I2,J2) = A(I2,J2) + 1.0
43080 CONTINUE


C         THE RESTRUCTURED
          DO 43081  I = 1, N
              I1 = D(1,I)
              J1 = D(2,I)
              I1 =          1 + MOD2N(I1,64)
              J1 =          1 + MOD2N(J1,64)
          D(3,I)   = D(3,I) + B(I1,J1)
          D(4,I)   = D(4,I) + C(I1,J1)
          D(1,I)   = D(1,I) + D(3,I)
          D(2,I)   = D(2,I) + D(4,I)
              I2 = D(1,I)
              J2 = D(2,I)
              I2 =              MOD2N(I2,64)
              J2 =              MOD2N(J2,64)
          D(1,I)   = D(1,I) + G(J2+32)
          D(2,I)   = D(2,I) + H(J2+32)
          I2V(I)   = I2     + E(I2+32)
          J2V(I)   = J2     + F(J2+32)
43081 CONTINUE

          DO 43082 I = 1, N
              I2       = I2V(I)
              J2       = J2V(I)
          A(I2,J2) = A(I2,J2) + 1.0
43082 CONTINUE
```

In loop 43090 the last two lines are recursive, because A(I−1) is used in the computation of B(I), which is then used to compute A(I). All previous lines in the loop can be vectorized. Splitting the loop as shown by loops 43091 and 43092 requires propagating the values of scalars RLDI and RLD1. Since the second is a simple function of the first, the array VRLDI is introduced to carry values between the loops, and RLD1 is recomputed in the second loop. Figure 4.14 shows an improvement of about 50% for the restructuring.

```
C       THE ORIGINAL
        DO 43090 I = 2, N
        RLD     = C(I) - B(I)
        RLDI    = 1. / RLD
        RLD1    = RLDI + 1.0
        D(I,1)  = (D(I,1) - RLD1   *   D(I,4))   *   RLDI
        D(I,2)  = (D(I,2) - RLD1   *   D(I,4))   *   RLDI
        D(I,3)  = (D(I,3) - RLD1   *   D(I,4))   *   RLDI
        B(I)    = (D(I,4) - RLD1   *   A(I-1))   *   RLDI
        A(I)    = E(I)  *   RLDI   *   B(I)
43090 CONTINUE

C       THE RESTRUCTURED
        DO 43091 I = 2, N
        RLD       = C(I) - B(I)
        VRLDI(I)  = 1. / RLD
        RLD1      = VRLDI(I) + 1.0
        D(I,1)    = (D(I,1) - RLD1   *   D(I,4))   *   VRLDI(I)
        D(I,2)    = (D(I,2) - RLD1   *   D(I,4))   *   VRLDI(I)
        D(I,3)    = (D(I,3) - RLD1   *   D(I,4))   *   VRLDI(I)
43091 CONTINUE

        DO 43092 I = 2, N
        RLD1 = VRLDI(I) + 1.0
        B(I) = (D(I,4) - RLD1   *   A(I-1))   *   VRLDI(I)
        A(I) = E(I)  *   VRLDI(I)   *   B(I)
43092 CONTINUE
```

We stated several times in earlier sections that simple one-dimensional recursion cannot be vectorized, as in loop 43099.

```
        DO 43099 I = 2, N
        A(I) = 2.0 * A(I-1) + B(I)
43099 CONTINUE
```

But as soon as a second dimension is involved, there are ways to restructure the loops to force the recursion into an outer loop, allowing the inner loop to vectorize. For example, loop 43100 is recursive in I but not in J. So reversing the order of the loops as shown in 43101–43102 allows the compiler to issue vector instructions for the inner loop.

The only problem to be resolved is how to compute all the values assumed by AH in the original outer loop and retain them for use when the loop nest is inverted. Again this is resolved by promoting the scalar AH to a vector VAH and precomputing all of the needed values in loop 43101. Note

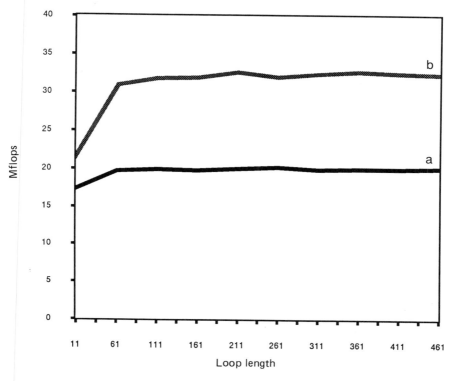

FIGURE 4.14
Performance Comparison of Loops 43090 and 43091, Cray
X-MP. a, original; b, restructured.

that as a side effect of loop switching the code originally contained in the
outer loop is also now vectorized.

```
C       THE ORIGINAL
        DO 43100 J = 1, N
        AH = B(J) - B(J-1)
        DO 43100 I = 2, N
          A(I,J) = AH * A(I-1,J) + C(I,J)
43100 CONTINUE

C       THE RESTRUCTURED
        DO 43101 J = 1, N
        VAH(J) = B(J) - B(J-1)
43101 CONTINUE

        DO 43102 I = 2, N
         DO 43102 J = 1, N
          A(I,J) = VAH(J) * A(I-1,J) + C(I,J)
43102 CONTINUE
```

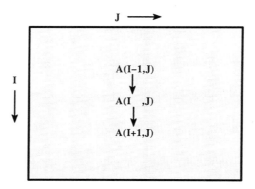

FIGURE 4.15
Loop 43100: Recursive Inner Loop on Columns of A

Figure 4.15 illustrates that the inner loop 43100 is processing a *single* column of the array A, and that each element calculated feeds directly into the next loop iteration. With the loops switched, as in 43102, the inner loop on J is generating the Ith row of the array A from the (I−1)st row, as shown in Figure 4.16. The recurrence has been pushed into the outer loop, allowing the inner loop to fully vectorize. Graphing the megaflop rates for loops 43100 and 43102, Figure 4.17 depicts a performance improvement for the restructured code approaching a factor of seven for long vectors.

When a single array reference appears to be recursive in all dimensions, as in loop 43139, it is in fact *not* recursive within the vectorizable inner loop.

```
       DO 43139 J = 1,M
          DO 43139 I = 1, N
             A(I,J) = 2.0 * A(I-1,J-1) + Y(I,J)
43139 CONTINUE
```

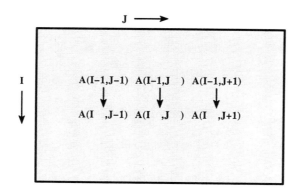

FIGURE 4.16
Loop 43102: Nonrecursive Inner Loop on Rows of A

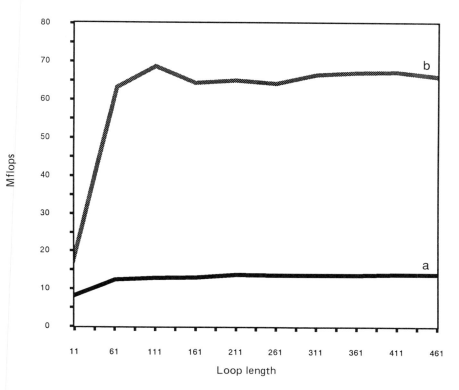

FIGURE 4.17
Performance Comparison of Loops 43100 and 43101 – 43102,
Cray X-MP. a, original; b, restructured.

In loop 43139 the inner loop on I is computing the Jth column of A from the
entirely separate vector in the (J—1)st column. This is depicted in Figure 4.18.

A more difficult problem appears when the inner loop contains one
recursive term for each of the dimensions of the problem. This arises often in
implicit solution techniques where the update of the current point in the grid
involves the previously computed neighbor points. Loop 43140 is an example of this in two dimensions. The left and top boundary values in A remain
fixed, and the loop computes the interior points. This is typically embedded
in an iterative loop that supplies an initial guess for the interior point values
and checks for convergence from one iteration to the next.

```
C       THE ORIGINAL
        DIMENSION A(N,N,3), B(N,N), C(N,N)
            . . .
        DO 43140 J = 2, N
        DO 43140 I = 2, N
```

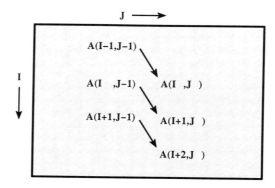

FIGURE 4.18
Loop 43139: Nonrecursive Inner Loop on Columns of A

```
        A(I,J,1) = A(I,J,1) - B(I,J) * A(I-1,J,1)
      *                     - C(I,J) * A(I,J-1,1)
        A(I,J,2) = A(I,J,2) - B(I,J) * A(I-1,J,2)
      *                     - C(I,J) * A(I,J-1,2)
        A(I,J,3) = A(I,J,3) - B(I,J) * A(I-1,J,3)
      *                     - C(I,J) * A(I,J-1,3)
43140 CONTINUE
```

As written, loop 43140 will not vectorize, because A(I,J,1) depends on A(I−1,J,1). [The same statement is true for the other assignments into A(I,J,2) and A(I,J,3).] Nor will it vectorize if the loops are switched, because A(I,J,1) depends also on A(I,J−1,1). This is depicted in Figure 4.19.

There is a way out of this apparently hopeless situation. If we view the

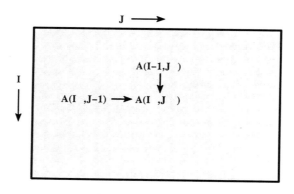

FIGURE 4.19
Loop 43140: Fully Recursive in Both Dimensions of A

algorithm in terms of diagonals on the grid, instead of rows or columns, then
the following dependencies exist:

- The new value at the point A(2,2,1) depends on the values of the
  boundary points A(2,1,1) and A(1,2,1):

```
            A(1,2,1)

               ┆

A(2,1,1)--A(2,2,1)--

               ┆
```

- The next diagonal (A(2,3,1), A(3,2,1)) can be computed from the
  newly generated value for A(2,2,1) and the other points on the diagonal A(3,1,1), A(2,2,1), A(1,3,1):

```
                A(1,3,1)

                   ┆

    A(2,2,1)--A(2,3,1)--

        ┆          ┆

A(3,1,1)--A(3,2,1)--

               ┆
```

In general, the values on any one diagonal depend on the newly
computed values on the diagonal to the left. Most important of all, none of
the diagonal points depend on any of the other points on the same diagonal.
So if we can find a way to express this in a nested Fortran DO loop, we will
have a vectorizable inner loop, with the recursion (on diagonals) existing
totally in the outer loop. Loop 43141 is one way of writing this. It retains the
assignment statement for A from loop 43140 but indexes both I and J in the
inner loop.

```
C       THE RESTRUCTURED
        DIMENSION A(N,N,3), B(N,N), C(N,N)
          . . .
        NDIAGS = 2 * N - 3
        ISTART = 1
        JSTART = 2
        LDIAG  = 0
        DO 43141 IDIAGS = 1, NDIAGS
         IF(IDIAGS .LE. N-1 ) THEN
            ISTART = ISTART + 1
            LDIAG  = LDIAG  + 1
         ELSE
            JSTART = JSTART + 1
            LDIAG  = LDIAG  - 1
```

```
          ENDIF
          I = ISTART + 1
          J = JSTART - 1
CDIR$ IVDEP
CVD$ NODEPCHK
*VDIR NODEP
          DO 43142 IPOINT = 1, LDIAG
          I = I - 1
          J = J + 1
          A(I,J,1) = A(I,J,1) - B(I,J) * A(I-1,J,1)
     *                        - C(I,J) * A(I,J-1,1)
          A(I,J,2) = A(I,J,2) - B(I,J) * A(I-1,J,2)
     *                        - C(I,J) * A(I,J-1,2)
          A(I,J,3) = A(I,J,3) - B(I,J) * A(I-1,J,3)
     *                        - C(I,J) * A(I,J-1,3)
43142 CONTINUE
43141 CONTINUE
```

Figure 4.20 illustrates the diagonals being calculated. Loop 43141 calculates the indexes of the left-most point at which a diagonal begins and calls these indexes ISTART and JSTART. The number of points on each diagonal is then computed and assigned to LDIAG. Index J is incremented, and I decrements within the inner loop.

This representation has potential for recursion when viewed by a compiler, so we include directives immediately before the inner loop to indicate that it is safe to vectorize it. The directives indicate to a compiler that no recursive dependencies occur within the loop, and they appear as comments to any other compiler.

Figure 4.21 demonstrates a performance improvement approaching a

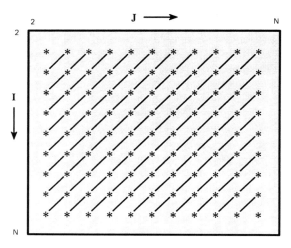

FIGURE 4.20
Diagonals Being Accessed by Loops 43141 and 43142

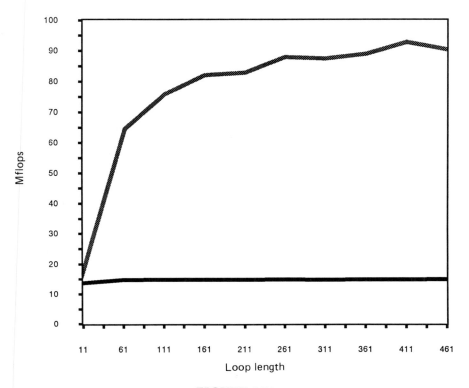

FIGURE 4.21
Performance Comparison of Loops 43140 and 43141–43142,
Cray X-MP. Original, solid line; restructured, dotted line.

factor of ten for long vector lengths, when vectorizing on diagonals. Note that for this particular example we used the CFT1.15 compiler, because CFT 77 would not vectorize the restructured loop even with the IVDEP directive.

It should be obvious that this approach has added initialization overhead that must somehow be amortized to achieve a performance improvement over the original. We are trying to realize the improvement by the inherent speed advantage of vector-versus-scalar instructions. Thus, we should be able to estimate the improvement based on our knowledge of vector length and the crossover point between vector and scalar performance on any machine.

Note that the vector length of the diagonals in loop 43142 varies from one to $N - 1$. We compute the average vector length of the diagonals as: Let:

$$NP = \text{number of computed points}$$
$$= (N - 1)^2$$

ND = number of diagonals

$\quad\;\; = 2N - 1$

Then

$$VL_{avg} = \frac{(N-1)^2}{(2N-1)}$$

It is left as an exercise for the reader to derive the average vector length on a general rectangular grid. The important thing to note in the equation is that the average vector length is always less than the dimension of the problem. So to be effective, this technique must have good performance for vectors in this range. For example, a 50×50 grid has an average vector length of $49 \times 49/99 = 24.3$. So on a machine that has good vector/scalar performance ratio for vector length 24, there is a payoff for vectorizing on the diagonals. We like to use a minimum factor of two performance improvement as a rule of thumb for applying this scheme.

It is natural to ask whether this technique applies to problems of greater-than-two dimensions, and in fact it does. Imagine a three-dimensional model in which we start at one corner and take planar slices at 45° angles to all axes (Figure 4.22). Immediately, we should notice that these slices do not result in the simple vectors of the two-dimensional scheme — that is, the slices do not have a constant stride between successive points. In general the planar slices are triangular. But the points on the planes are not recursive among themselves, and very quickly the number of points on a plane grows very large. In fact, for a $50 \times 50 \times 50$ grid, the average number of points on a slice exceeds 800. There can be a tremendous payoff for vectorizing this computation if run on a machine with vector-indirect address

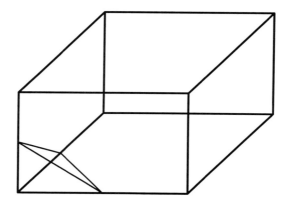

FIGURE 4.22
Planar Slices Through a Three-Dimensional Model

instructions — that is, a machine with gather/scatter hardware. Any number of dimensions can be treated in this manner, with the number of points on a slice (i.e., the vector length) growing exponentially with the number of dimensions.

4.9.5   Scalar Recursion

In loop 43149, the scalar variable SIA fits our definition of recursion. That is, the value of SIA computed in one iteration feeds into the subsequent iteration.

```
            SIA = 0.
            DO 43149 I = 1, N
              SIA = SIA + 2.0
              A(I) = SIA * B(I)
      43149 CONTINUE
```

But if we note that SIA is a constant-increment variable as defined in Section 3.3.2 and is assuming the sequence of values 2.0, 4.0, . . . , N * 2.0, then it should be clear that a compiler can treat SIA as a vector by generating the sequence either in memory or in a vector register, then setting SIA to N * 2.0 after the loop terminates. If we have such a construct in a loop and the compiler refuses to vectorize it, you should ask the vendor to correct this.

Suppose that SIA is a true reduction function (not a CIV) — such as the sum of the elements of a vectorizable expression — and that SIA is used in another expression as well, as in loop 43150.

```
      C        THE ORIGINAL
               SIA = 0.0
               J = 1
               DO 43150 I = 1, N, 2
                 SIA = SIA + A(I,MM) * B(I) + A(I+1,MM) * B(I+1)
                 C(J) = SIA * D(J,MM)
                 J = J + 1
         43150 CONTINUE
```

A compiler can generate the final answer for SIA in a vectorized/optimized manner but cannot simultaneously generate the intermediate sums needed in the other expression, so the loop will be executed in scalar mode. But we can split the loop into three parts, one that computes the elements of the vectorizable expression, a second that computes the partial sums, and a third that can vectorize the computation of C. This is shown in loops 43151, 43152, and 43153.

```
      C        THE RESTRUCTURED
               J = 1
               DO 43151 I = 1, N+1
                 SIAT(I) = A(I,MM) * B(I)
         43151 CONTINUE
```

```
        PSIAV(1) = SIAT(1)
        DO 43152 I = 2, N+1
         PSIAV(I) = PSIAV(I-1) + SIAT(I)
43152   CONTINUE

        DO 43153 I = 1, N, 2
         C(J) = PSIAV(I+1) * D(J,MM)
         J = J + 1
43153   CONTINUE
```

Here, the recursion has been isolated down to its minimal operation in loop 43152—a loop that cannot be vectorized but can be highly optimized by many compilers. All of the other operations are now fully vectorized in loops 43151 and 43153.

The two important techniques we used to restructure loop 43150 are called "loop splitting" and "scalar promotion." The scalar variable SIA was promoted to a vector PSIAV, and the loop was split to isolate the recursion. Figure 4.23 depicts a performance improvement approaching a factor of four for this restructuring.

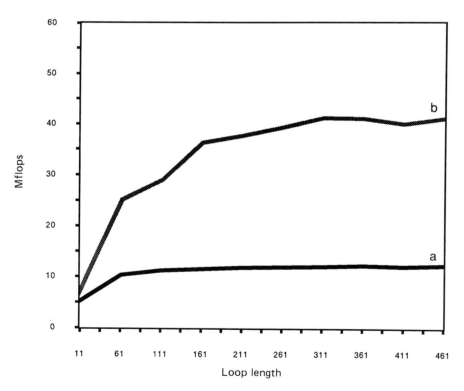

FIGURE 4.23
Performance Comparison of Loops 43150 and 43151–43153,
Cray X-MP. a, original; b, restructured.

SIA in the preceding example is a zero-dimensional variable promoted to a one-dimensional array. In general it is often advantageous to promote an n-dimensional entity to an $(n + 1)$-dimensional array if this removes recursion from the inner loop of the code. The restructuring of loop 43200 demonstrates this.

```
        RECUR(1) = 0.
        DO 43200 J = 1, M
         DO 43200 I = 2, N
          A(I,J)    = SQRT (Y(I,J)**2 + Z(I,J)**2)
          RECUR(I) = A(I,J) + RECUR(I-1) * B(I,J)
          C(I,J)    = RECUR(I) + EXP (D(I,J))
43200 CONTINUE
```

The single-dimension recursion of RECUR appears intractable at first glance. Note however that for each iteration on J, RECUR receives a new sequence of values. No data carries from one iteration of J to the next, because RECUR(1) = 0. and it is never changed. If we promote RECUR to a two-dimensional array, then we can switch the nesting of the loops and push the recursion into the outer loop, as shown in loop 43202.

```
        DIMENSION VRECUR (ndim1A,ndim2a)
          . . .
        DO 43201 J = 1, M
          VRECUR(1,J) = 0.
43201 CONTINUE

        DO 43202 I = 2, N
         DO 43202 J = 1,M
          A(I,J)      = SQRT (Y(I,J)**2 + Z(I,J)**2)
          VRECUR(I,J) = A(I,J) + VRECUR(I-1,J) * B(I,J)
          C(I,J)      = VRECUR(I,J) + EXP (D(I,J))
43202 CONTINUE
```

In the original loop, RECUR assumed M different sequences, one at a time. In the new loop, all M sequences are being developed together, one term at a time in the inner loop. The fact that each sequence must begin with a zero term necessitates loop 43201 to initialize each of the M sequences. The values "ndim1A" and "ndim2A" are so named to indicate that the dimensions of the array A will be sufficient for VRECUR.

It is extremely unlikely that the values of RECUR would be used after such a loop. But for completeness, loops 43203 and 43204 demonstrate saving the last values for subsequent use.

```
        DIMENSION VRECUR (ndim1A,ndim2a)
          . . .
        DO 43201 J = 1, M
          VRECUR(1,J) = 0.
43201 CONTINUE
```

```
        DO 43204 I = 2, N
        DO 43203 J = 1,M
        A(I,J)    = SQRT (Y(I,J)**2 + Z(I,J)**2)
        VRECUR(I,J) = A(I,J) + VRECUR(I-1,J) * B(I,J)
        C(I,J)    = VRECUR(I,J) + EXP (D(I,J))
43203 CONTINUE
        RECUR(I) = VRECUR(I,M)
43204 CONTINUE
```

Loop switching sometimes introduces memory-bank conflicts, since the stride is now across rather than down the columns. So as a final restructuring, eliminate such conflicts if necessary.

Wrap-Around Scalars

Many wrap-around scalars are simply holding a value from the last iteration to act as one side of a moving interval within the loop, as in 43210.

```
        TOP = 0.
        DO 43210 I = 1, N
        BOT = TOP
        TOP = X(I) * B(I)
        Y(I) = Y(I) + Z(I) / (TOP - BOT)
43210 CONTINUE
```

If a compiler balks at vectorizing this, consider rewriting as shown in loop 43211, where the first iteration has been written out in scalar mode (to handle the initial value of zero for BOT), and the defining expression for TOP has been substituted in the loop for both TOP and BOT.

```
        Y(1) = (Y(1) + Z(1)) / ( X(1) * B(1))
        DO 43211 I = 2,N
        Y(I) = Y(I) + Z(I) / (X(I) * B(I) - X(I-1) * B(I-1))
43211 CONTINUE
```

As a second alternative, TOP can be promoted to a vector, and BOT can be eliminated, as shown in loop 43212.

```
        DIMENSION VTOP (0:ndimX)
            . . .
        VTOP(0) = 0.
        DO 43212 I = 1, N
        VTOP(I) = X(I) * B(I)
        Y(I) = Y(I) + Z(I) / (VTOP(I) - VTOP(I-1))
43212 CONTINUE
```

Although both of the preceding restructurings will vectorize, each has its advantages and disadvantages, depending on the target computer system. Loop 43211 provides vectorization at the cost of adding a multiply operation as well as fetching the vectors X and B twice. Loop 43212 adds no arithmetic operations, but requires storing and fetching the vector VTOP. As we try these techniques on a particular machine, we will develop a feel for which works better for our programs.

Sometimes the elimination of a wrap-around scalar leads to even further optimization of a loop. As long as we are rewriting the loop we may as well analyze the algorithm to see if it is as efficient as it can be. Consider loop 44020:

```
        BR = 0.
        DO 44020 I = 1, N
          BL = BR
          BR = (I-1) * DELB
          A(I) = (BR - BL) * C(I) + (BR**2 - BL**2) * C(I)**2
44020   CONTINUE
```

If we were to apply the same techniques as in loop 43212, we would promote BR to a vector and eliminate BL. Closer inspection reveals that the expression (BR − BL) is equal to DELB for all but the first iteration, so computing the difference is a wasted operation in the loop. With that term removed, then note that only the squared terms remain. In fact, BL**2 is recomputing the values of BR**2 from the previous iteration. Finally, note that the computation is a polynomial evaluation, for which factoring will reduce operations and enhance chaining. Therefore a better restructuring is outlined in loop 44022.

```
C       THE RESTRUCTURED
        B       = 0.0
        BSQ(1) = 0.0
        A(1)    = 0.0
        DO 44022 I = 2, N
        B       = B + DELB
        BSQ(I) = B**2
        A(I)    = C(I) * ( DELB + C(I) * (BSQ(I) - BSQ(I-1)))
44022 CONTINUE
```

This restructuring vectorizes and reduces the number of arithmetic operations from ten to six. Note that a compiler will recognize B as a CIV and not treat it as a wrap-around scalar or as a reduction-function scalar. This allows its use in the line following its definition. Figure 4.24 indicates a performance improvement that exceeds a factor of 15 for this restructuring.

Our restructuring assumes that the final values of BL and BR are not needed elsewhere in the program. If such last-value saving were necessary, it could be accomplished by inserting the following lines after loop 44022:

```
BL = (N-2) * DELB

BR = (N-1) * DELB
```

When scalars are defined conditionally, they also have the potential to wrap around from one iteration to the next. In loop 44025, whenever the

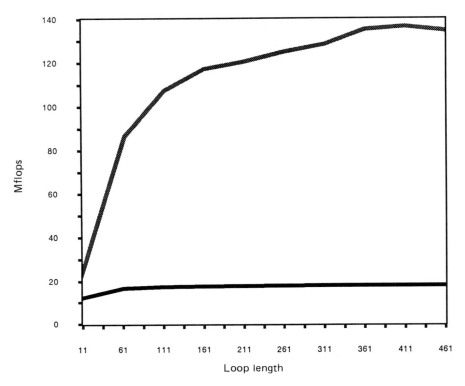

FIGURE 4.24
Performance Comparison of Loops 44020 and 44022, Cray
X-MP. Original, solid line; restructured, dotted line.

condition A(I) .GT. 0. is false, the value used for SCA in the assignments to
B(I) and E(I) is from the previous iteration.

```
      SCA = 0.
      DO 44025 I = 1, N
       IF (A(I) .GT.  0.) THEN
         SCA = X(I) * Y(I)
       ENDIF
       B(I) = SCA * C(I) + D(I)
       E(I) = (SCA + 1.0) * Z(I)
44025 CONTINUE
```

Suppose that every third value of A is greater than zero, then SCA
assumes the sequence of values:

```
X(1)*Y(1), X(1)*Y(1), X(1)*Y(1), X(4)*Y(4), X(4)*Y(4), . . .
```

Since the compiler cannot know when the condition will be true, it is almost
impossible to generate the sequence of values in vector mode. In fact, if SCA
were promoted to a vector of values and its setting were isolated in a separate

loop, then the recursion should become obvious, as in loops 44026 and 44027.

```
        VSCA(1) = 0.
        DO 44026 I = 1, N
         IF (A(I) .GT.  0.) THEN
          VSCA(I) = X(I) * Y(I)
         ELSE
          VSCA(I) = VSCA(I-1)
         ENDIF
44026 CONTINUE

        DO 44027 I = 1, N
         B(I) = VSCA(I) * C(I) + D(I)
         E(I) = (VSCA(I) + 1.0) * Z(I)
44027 CONTINUE
```

Whether or not there is a payoff for this restructuring depends on how many times SCA is used in the loop, so we must experiment with each loop for which this technique applies.

Loop 44030 provides an additional twist to the problem of the wrap-around scalar. Not only is PF referenced before it is set, but once set, it is sometimes reset within an iteration under control of the IF statement. Promoting PF to a vector and eliminating PB once again removes the recursion, as shown in loop 44031. Here, the speedup is about a factor of five over the original code, as depicted in Figure 4.25.

```
C       THE ORIGINAL
        PF = 0.0
        DO 44030 I = 2, N
        AV   = B(I) * RV
        PB   = PF
        PF   = C(I)
        IF ((D(I) + D(I+1)) .LT.  0.) PF = -C(I+1)
        AA   = E(I) - E(I-1) + F(I) - F(I-1)
       1     + G(I) + G(I-1) - H(I) - H(I-1)
        BB   = R(I) + S(I-1) + T(I) + T(I-1)
       1     - U(I) - U(I-1) + V(I) + V(I-1)
       2     - W(I) + W(I-1) - X(I) + X(I-1)
        A(I) = AV * (AA + BB + PF - PB + Y(I) - Z(I)) + A(I)
44030 CONTINUE

C       THE RESTRUCTURED
        VPF(1) = 0.0
        DO 44031 I = 2, N
        AV    = B(I) * RV
        VPF(I) = C(I)
        IF ((D(I) + D(I+1)) .LT.  0.) VPF(I) = -C(I+1)
        AA   = E(I) - E(I-1) + F(I) - F(I-1)
       1     + G(I) + G(I-1) - H(I) - H(I-1)
        BB   = R(I) + S(I-1) + T(I) + T(I-1)
       1     - U(I) - U(I-1) + V(I) + V(I-1)
       2     - W(I) + W(I-1) - X(I) + X(I-1)
        A(I) = AV * (AA + BB + VPF(I) - VPF(I-1) + Y(I) - Z(I)) + A(I)
44031 CONTINUE
```

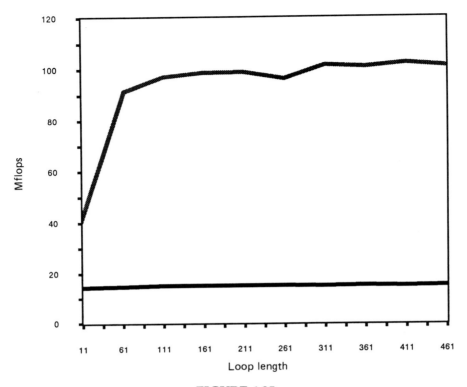

FIGURE 4.25
Performance Comparison of Loops 44030 and 44031, Cray
X-MP. Original, solid line; restructured, dotted line.

In loop 44040 there are two problems with scalars. First, SIGMAX is a wrap-around scalar in that it is referenced in the IF statement, then subsequently set. If a compiler tried to vectorize this as written it would have the additional problem of not knowing whether SIGMAX is set in any particular iteration. A smart enough compiler might recognize that SIGMAX is actually a reduction function, and it could generate optimized code that produces the final answer for SIGMAX.

Unfortunately, only a few compilers will handle the second problem, which is the setting of IMAX to the index of the maximum value. Consequently, those compilers unable to optimize finding the value of IMAX will leave the entire loop unoptimized. Our restructuring in loop 44041 splits out the vectorizable code from the top of the loop and promotes SIGABC to a vector VSIGABC to propagate the values to loop 44042 where the maximum and its index are computed. Most vendors provide a system library routine that can further optimize loop 44042.

Figure 4.26 shows that the restructured loops outperform the original by about a factor of six. So, if the bulk of our CPU time is spent in such loops, this restructuring will reduce an hour down to ten minutes.

```
C       THE ORIGINAL
        DO 44040 I = 2, N
        RR          = 1.  / A(I,1)
        U           = A(I,2) * RR
        V           = A(I,3) * RR
        W           = A(I,4) * RR
        SNDSP       = SQRT (GD * (A(I,5) * RR + .5* (U*U + V*V + W*W)))
        SIGA        = ABS (XT + U*B(I) + V*C(I) + W*D(I))
     *              + SNDSP * SQRT (B(I)**2 + C(I)**2 + D(I)**2)
        SIGB        = ABS (YT + U*E(I) + V*F(I) + W*G(I))
     *              + SNDSP * SQRT (E(I)**2 + F(I)**2 + G(I)**2)
        SIGC        = ABS (ZT + U*H(I) + V*R(I) + W*S(I))
     *              + SNDSP * SQRT (H(I)**2 + R(I)**2 + S(I)**2)
        SIGABC      = AMAX1 (SIGA, SIGB, SIGC)
        IF (SIGABC .GT. SIGMAX) THEN
          IMAX      = I
          SIGMAX    = SIGABC
        ENDIF
44040 CONTINUE


C       THE RESTRUCTURED
        DO 44041 I = 2, N
        RR          = 1.  / A(I,1)
        U           = A(I,2) * RR
        V           = A(I,3) * RR
        W           = A(I,4) * RR
        SNDSP       = SQRT (GD * (A(I,5) * RR + .5* (U*U + V*V + W*W)))
        SIGA        = ABS (XT + U*B(I) + V*C(I) + W*D(I))
     *              + SNDSP * SQRT (B(I)**2 + C(I)**2 + D(I)**2)
        SIGB        = ABS (YT + U*E(I) + V*F(I) + W*G(I))
     *              + SNDSP * SQRT (E(I)**2 + F(I)**2 + G(I)**2)
        SIGC        = ABS (ZT + U*H(I) + V*R(I) + W*S(I))
     *              + SNDSP * SQRT (H(I)**2 + R(I)**2 + S(I)**2)
        VSIGABC(I)  = AMAX1 (SIGA, SIGB, SIGC)
44041 CONTINUE

        DO 44042 I = 2, N
        IF (VSIGABC(I) .GT.  SIGMAX) THEN
          IMAX      = I
          SIGMAX    = VSIGABC(I)
        ENDIF
44042 CONTINUE
```

Loop 44050 is the classically coded matrix multiply, just as we all learned it in linear algebra. That is, the inner loop is a dot product between a row of matrix B and a column of matrix C. Note that during execution of the inner loop the indexes I and J do not vary, so that A(I,J) acts just like a scalar. Most compilers recognize this dot product and use their optimized code to generate each result in A. All machines can perform the multiplication of a row of B with a column of C in vector mode, but the add operation must often be completed in scalar mode.

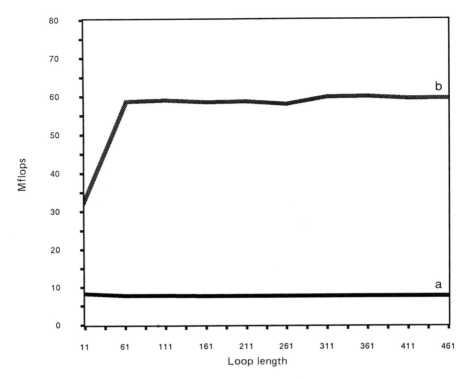

FIGURE 4.26
Performance Comparison of Loops 44040 and 44041–44042,
Cray X-MP. a, original; b, restructured.

```
C      THE ORIGINAL
       DO 44050 I = 1, N
       DO 44050 J = 1, N
       A(I,J) = 0.0
       DO 44050 K = 1, N
       A(I,J) = A(I,J) + B(I,K) * C(K,J)
44050 CONTINUE
```

Our restructuring in loops 44051 and 44052 splits out the array initialization into a separate vectorizable loop, then switches the order of the loop nest to make I the inner loop index, with K relegated to the outer loop. This causes the inner loop to be vector = vector + vector × scalar, or:

```
       A(I,J) = A(I,J) + B(I,J) * C(K,J)
```

which happens to be the best combination of operations for most supercomputers. This forces the recursion of the dot product into the outer loop.

Note that although the original loop fetched and stored each element of the array A only once, the restructuring fetches and stores each element of A "N" times. This is somewhat offset by a reduction of the number of fetches of each element of C from N down to one. Most machines have sufficient

memory paths that the restructuring outperforms the original. But machines
that have only one memory path might show no improvement. Our timing
on the Cray X-MP (Figure 4.27) represents a factor-of-two improvement.

```
C        THE RESTRUCTURED
         DO 44051 J = 1, N
         DO 44051 I = 1, N
         A(I,J) = 0.0
44051 CONTINUE

         DO 44052 K = 1, N
         DO 44052 J = 1, N
         DO 44052 I = 1, N
         A(I,J) = A(I,J) + B(I,K) * C(K,J)
44052 CONTINUE
```

Our final example in this section (loop 44060) appears to be even
simpler than the preceding matrix multiply, but an extra twist has been

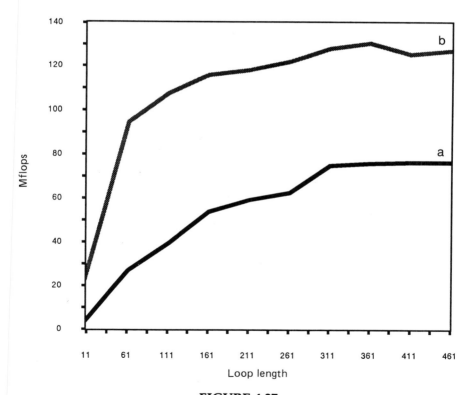

FIGURE 4.27
Performance Comparison of Loops 44050 and 44051–44052,
Cray X-MP. a, original; b, restructured.

added. This "convolution kernel" is computing N dot products, each consist-
ing of a row from the lower triangular matrix B dotted with a column from
the upper triangular matrix C. The upper triangle of B and the lower triangle
of C occupy memory but never enter the calculation.

```
C       THE ORIGINAL
        DO 44060 I = 1, N
        A(I) = 0.0
        DO 44060 J = 1, I
          A(I) = A(I) + B(I,J) * C(J,I)
44060 CONTINUE
```

The *outer* loop generates results as follows:

```
A(1) = B(1,1) * C(1,1)

A(2) = B(2,1) * C(1,2) + B(2,2) * C(2,2)

A(3) = B(3,1) * C(1,3) + B(3,2) * C(2,3) + B(3,3) * C(3,3)

                    . . .

A(N) = B(N,1) * C(1,N) + . . . + B(N,N) * C(N,N)
```

Again, the dot product is usually only partially vectorized, so we would like
to switch the loop nesting to cause the inner loop to run on I — thus allowing
full vectorization. But the length of the inner loop depends on the index of
the outer loop, so directly switching them as done in the matrix multiply
would produce nonsensical code:

```
DO ... J = 1, I
  DO ... I = 1, N
```

This restructuring requires a careful study of the interplay between the
two DO statements to determine how to switch them. Begin by noting that
the final outer iteration of the original loop is

```
DO 44060 I = ... N
  DO 44060 J = 1,N
```

From this we know that to switch the loops we must have an outer loop J that
runs from 1 to N. Working backward, now we can state that the only value of
I for which J = N is I = N. Again, J = N − 1 for two values of I: I = N − 1
and I = N. Working all the way back to J = 1, we see that this is true for all
values of I from one to N. Finally, we can see the pattern that, as shown in
loop nest 44062, as J ranges from 1 to N, I ranges from J to N. Once again the
dot product has been pushed into the outer loop, and the inner loop fully
vectorizes.

   In Figure 4.28, the performance improvement of about a factor of two
for moderate vector lengths diminishes to just above one for longer lengths.
This is because much of the addition in the original dot-product implementation can be performed in vector mode for longer vector lengths; only the

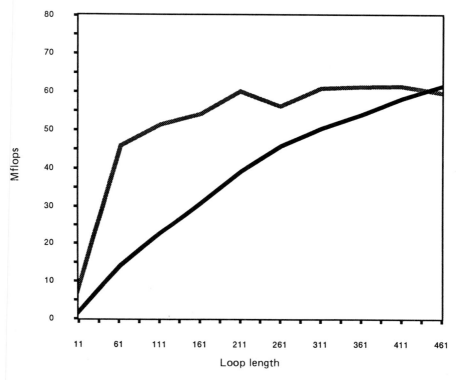

FIGURE 4.28
Performance Comparison of Loops 44060 and 44061–44062,
Cray X-MP. Original, solid line; restructured, dotted line.

final 64 or fewer elements in the last register computed must to be added in
scalar mode.

```
C       THE RESTRUCTURED
        DO 44061 I = 1, N
        A(I) = 0.0
44061 CONTINUE

        DO 44062 J = 1, N
        DO 44062 I = J, N
        A(I) = A(I) + B(I,J) * C(J,I)
44062 CONTINUE
```

4.9.6   More Loop Switching

The inner loops of the nest 45011, 45010 will be vectorized by essentially all
compilers, but performance will greatly depend on the vector length (un-
known to the compiler). The major computational loop, 45010, is summing

the elements of vectorizable expressions. We saw in the previous section that this has a good payoff only for long vector lengths. If we know that the outer loop on I has a vector length greater than or equal to the vector length of the inner loop on K, we must consider switching the nesting to achieve the best vector performance.

```
C       THE ORIGINAL
        DO 45011 I = 1, IM
        SUM1    = 0.0
        SUM2    = 0.0
        SUM4    = 0.0
        SUM5    = 0.0

        DO 45010 K = 2, KM
        KK      = KM - K + 1
        SUM1 = SUM1 + 4.0 * ( A(J+1,K ,I,1) * A(J+1,K ,I,6)
     *                +       A(J+1,KK,I,1) * A(J+1,KK,I,6) )
     *                -       A(J+2,K ,I,1) * A(J+2,K ,I,6)
     *                -       A(J+2,KK,I,1) * A(J+2,KK,I,6)

        SUM2 = SUM2 + 4.0 * ( A(J+1,K, I,2) * A(J+1,K, I,6)
     *                +       A(J+1,KK,I,2) * A(J+1,KK,I,6) )
     *                -       A(J+2,K, I,2) * A(J+2,K, I,6)
     *                -       A(J+2,KK,I,2) * A(J+2,KK,I,6)

        SUM4 = SUM4 + 4.0 * ( A(J+1,K, I,4) * A(J+1,K, I,6)
     *                +       A(J+1,KK,I,4) * A(J+1,KK,I,6) )
     *                -       A(J+2,K, I,4) * A(J+2,K, I,6)
     *                -       A(J+2,KK,I,4) * A(J+2,KK,I,6)

        SUM5 = SUM5 + 4.0 * ( A(J+1,K, I,5) * A(J+1,K, I,6)
     *                +       A(J+1,KK,I,5) * A(J+1,KK,I,6) )
     *                -       A(J+2,K, I,5) * A(J+2,K, I,6)
     *                -       A(J+2,KK,I,5) * A(J+2,KK,I,6)
45010      CONTINUE

        DO 45011 K = 2, KM
        A(J,K,I,1) = SUM1 / (6.0 * (KM-2) * A(J,K,I,6))
        A(J,K,I,2) = SUM2 / (6.0 * (KM-2) * A(J,K,I,6))
        A(J,K,I,3) = 0.0
        A(J,K,I,4) = SUM4 / (6.0 * (KM-2) * A(J,K,I,6))
        A(J,K,I,5) = SUM5 / (6.0 * (KM-2) * A(J,K,I,6))
45011 CONTINUE
```

Notice that each iteration of the outer loop produces new values for SUM1, SUM2, SUM4, and SUM5, and these are used subsequently in the inner loop 45011. To bring the I loop inside the loops on K, we must promote the four SUMs to vectors. Furthermore, we must assure ourselves that the values in the A array computed in loop 45011 in one iteration do not feed back into loop 45010 on a subsequent outer iteration. Note that although we do not know the value of J, we can see that the columns of A referenced in loop 45010 (J+1, J+2) are completely independent of the column J referenced in loop 45011.

With all this in mind, we present the restructured version, loops 45012,

45013, and 45014, all of which fully vectorize. Figure 4.29 represents the restructured performance versus two different executions of the original, one with KM = 5 and the other with KM = 75. In this figure the X-axis represents various values of IM.

The results are quite interesting. Where KM = 5, the restructuring is always faster. Where KM = 75, the restructured is faster when IM is greater than 30. Notice that one advantage of switching the loops is to remove the reduction-function scalars SUM1, SUM2, SUM4, SUM5 on the K loop. When we switch the loop and bring I on the inside, we have removed all reduction functions.

Note in Figure 4.29 that in this particular example we used CFT 1.15 because CFT 77 did not vectorize the original loop 45010. And we wished to compare vectorization of the reduction function scalars in the original with full vectorization after loop switching in the restructured.

```
C       THE RESTRUCTURED
        DO 45012 I = 1, IM
        VSUM1(I)    = 0.0
        VSUM2(I)    = 0.0
        VSUM4(I)    = 0.0
        VSUM5(I)    = 0.0
 45012 CONTINUE

        DO 45013  K = 2, KM
        KK          = KM - K + 1
        DO 45013 I = 1, IM
        VSUM1(I) = VSUM1(I) + 4.0 * ( A(J+1,K ,I,1) * A(J+1,K ,I,6)
     *                      +         A(J+1,KK,I,1) * A(J+1,KK,I,6) )
     *                      -         A(J+2,K ,I,1) * A(J+2,K ,I,6)
     *                      -         A(J+2,KK,I,1) * A(J+2,KK,I,6)

        VSUM2(I) = VSUM2(I) + 4.0 * ( A(J+1,K, I,2) * A(J+1,K, I,6)
     *                      +         A(J+1,KK,I,2) * A(J+1,KK,I,6) )
     *                      -         A(J+2,K, I,2) * A(J+2,K, I,6)
     *                      -         A(J+2,KK,I,2) * A(J+2,KK,I,6)

        VSUM4(I) = VSUM4(I) + 4.0 * ( A(J+1,K, I,4) * A(J+1,K, I,6)
     *                      +         A(J+1,KK,I,4) * A(J+1,KK,I,6) )
     *                      -         A(J+2,K, I,4) * A(J+2,K, I,6)
     *                      -         A(J+2,KK,I,4) * A(J+2,KK,I,6)

        VSUM5(I) = VSUM5(I) + 4.0 * ( A(J+1,K, I,5) * A(J+1,K, I,6)
     *                      +         A(J+1,KK,I,5) * A(J+1,KK,I,6) )
     *                      -         A(J+2,K, I,5) * A(J+2,K, I,6)
     *                      -         A(J+2,KK,I,5) * A(J+2,KK,I,6)
 45013 CONTINUE

        DO 45014  K = 2, KM
        DO 45014 I = 1, IM
        A(J,K,I,1) = VSUM1(I) / (6.0 * (KM-2) * A(J,K,I,6))
        A(J,K,I,2) = VSUM2(I) / (6.0 * (KM-2) * A(J,K,I,6))
        A(J,K,I,3) = 0.0
        A(J,K,I,4) = VSUM4(I) / (6.0 * (KM-2) * A(J,K,I,6))
        A(J,K,I,5) = VSUM5(I) / (6.0 * (KM-2) * A(J,K,I,6))
 45014 CONTINUE
```

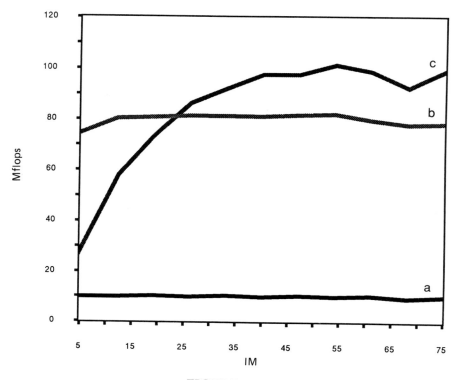

FIGURE 4.29
Performance Comparison of Loops 45011 and 45012–45014.
a, original (KM = 5); b, original (KM = 75); c, restructured.

Our last example of loop switching illustrates the value of vectorizing not only on the longest vector length, but of achieving vectorization of outer loop code as well. As before, most compilers will vectorize the inner loop on K, but its length is only five. It is important to always remember that just because a compiler informs us that it has vectorized an important loop in our program, there may be much improvement that can be attained. If we know, for example, that N is significantly larger than five, there is probably a payoff for inverting the loop nest to always have I be the inner-loop index.

```
C       THE ORIGINAL
        DO 45020 I = 1, N
        F(I) = A(I) + .5
        DO 45020 J = 1, 10
         D(I,J) = B(J) * F(I)
         DO 45020 K = 1, 5
          C(K,I,J) = D(I,J) * E(K)
45020 CONTINUE
```

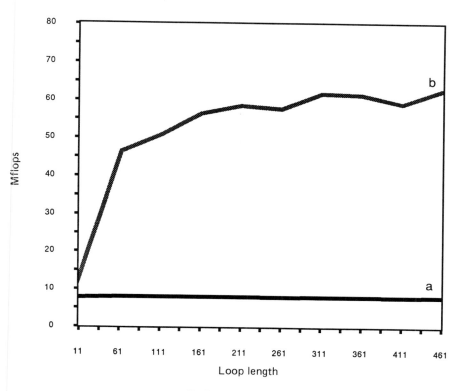

FIGURE 4.30

Performance Comparison of Loops 45020 and 45021−45023,
Cray X-MP. a, original; b, restructured.

To begin, we note that neither J nor K depend on I, and so the loops
may be easily switched. Next, we extract all code between one DO statement
and the next and place it into its own loop, always with I as the inner-loop
index. Finally, we can invert the nesting of the original inner-loop code, with
the result that all of the code in the original outer loop is now being executed
in vectorizable inner loops with long vector lengths, as shown in loops
45021, 45022, and 45023. Figure 4.30 shows that this restructuring outperforms the original by more than a factor of ten for long vector lengths.

```
C        THE RESTRUCTURED
         DO 45021 I = 1,N
           F(I) = A(I) + .5
45021 CONTINUE

         DO 45022 J = 1, 10
         DO 45022 I = 1, N
           D(I,J) = B(J) * F(I)
```

```
45022 CONTINUE

      DO 45023 K = 1, 5
        DO 45023 J = 1, 10
          DO 45023 I = 1, N
            C(K,I,J) = D(I,J) * E(K)
45023 CONTINUE
```

4.9.7 Loop Unrolling

Short loops often generate more overhead instructions than computational instructions. Because of this, many compilers will automatically unroll loops of small literal constant length. Our knowledge of algorithms can often be used to manually carry this idea to even better optimizations, especially when, as in loops 46010 and 46020, the inner loop contains few operations. As written, it is difficult for a compiler to make use of all the machine's registers and data paths.

```
C     THE ORIGINAL
      DO 46011 J = 1, 4
        DO 46010 I = 1, N
          C(J,I)=0.0
46010 CONTINUE

      DO 46011 K = 1, 4
        DO 46011 I = 1, N
          C(J,I) = C(J,I) + A(J,K) * B(K,I)
46011 CONTINUE
```

In this example the inner DO loop does vectorize on a nice, long vector length; but, there is room for additional improvement. Whenever small and explicit outer loops exist, as in loop 46011, they should be unrolled inside the larger vectorized loop. Note that the outer loop on J simply defines four equations in the C array:

```
C(1,I) =

C(2,I) =

C(3,I) =

C(4,I) =
```

Likewise, the outer loop on K simply generates four terms to be added into C for each value of J. In fact, when the loop on K is unrolled, there is no longer any need to initialize C to zero, and it no longer appears on the right side in the restructured loop 46012.

```
C     THE RESTRUCTURED
      DO 46012 I = 1, N
        C(1,I) = A(1,1) * B(1,I) + A(1,2) * B(2,I)
     *         + A(1,3) * B(3,I) + A(1,4) * B(4,I)
        C(2,I) = A(2,1) * B(1,I) + A(2,2) * B(2,I)
```

```
*              + A(2,3) * B(3,I) + A(2,4) * B(4,I)
     C(3,I) = A(3,1) * B(1,I) + A(3,2) * B(2,I)
*              + A(3,3) * B(3,I) + A(3,4) * B(4,I)
     C(4,I) = A(4,1) * B(1,I) + A(4,2) * B(2,I)
*              + A(4,3) * B(3,I) + A(4,4) * B(4,I)
46012 CONTINUE
```

This restructuring gives the compiler more calculations to optimize, thus obtaining more overlapping of functional units in the CPU. It also reduces memory traffic, because each time one of the vectors in B is fetched, it is reused four times.

This unrolling, shown in Figure 4.31, outperforms the original by about a factor of three. In loop 46020 the compiler will vectorize on the innermost loop, which contains a reduction function of length four. If vectorization of this loop is prevented with a compiler directive, it will actually run faster in

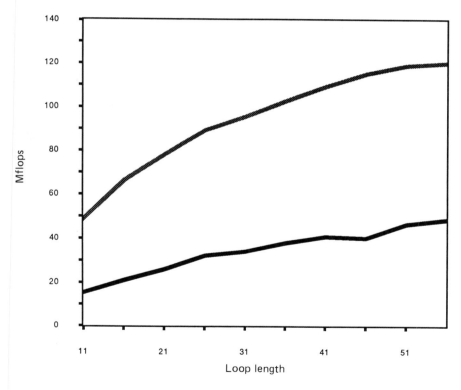

FIGURE 4.31

Performance Comparison of Loops 46011 and 46012, Cray X-MP. Original, solid line; restructured, dotted line.

scalar mode than in vector mode. The best approach is to restructure as shown in loop 46021.

```
C       THE ORIGINAL
        DO 46020 I = 1,N
        DO 46020 J = 1,4
        A(I,J) = 0.
        DO 46020 K = 1,4
          A(I,J) = A(I,J) + B(I,K) * C(K,J)
46020 CONTINUE


C       THE RESTRUCTURED
        DO 46021 I = 1, N
        A(I,1) = B(I,1) * C(1,1) + B(I,2) * C(2,1)
      *          + B(I,3) * C(3,1) + B(I,4) * C(4,1)
        A(I,2) = B(I,1) * C(1,2) + B(I,2) * C(2,2)
      *          + B(I,3) * C(3,2) + B(I,4) * C(4,2)
        A(I,3) = B(I,1) * C(1,3) + B(I,2) * C(2,3)
      *          + B(I,3) * C(3,3) + B(I,4) * C(4,3)
        A(I,4) = B(I,1) * C(1,4) + B(I,2) * C(2,4)
      *          + B(I,3) * C(3,4) + B(I,4) * C(4,4)
46021 CONTINUE
```

In the restructuring, loop 46021 shows the loops on J and K completely unrolled in the I loop. That is, the only effect of the original J loop was to choose four different columns of the A and C arrays to be computed as the sum of four terms indexed by the K loop. In the unrolling, all four equations and all four terms are explicitly written out, thus eliminating the need to initialize the elements of A to zero and allowing all of the code to fully vectorize.

Figure 4.32 shows an improvement of more than a factor of 30 for this restructuring.

In loops 44050, 44051, and 44052 we examined a restructuring of the traditionally coded matrix multiply into fully vectorized loops. Here, we reproduce the code of 44051 and 44052 as 46030 and 46031 to demonstrate the value of unrolling in such a set of nested loops.

```
C       THE ORIGINAL
        DO 46030 J  = 1, N
        DO 46030 I  = 1, N
        A(I,J) = 0.
46030 CONTINUE

        DO 46031   K = 1, N
        DO 46031   J = 1, N
        DO 46031 I = 1, N
          A(I,J) = A(I,J) + B(I,K) * C(K,J)
46031 CONTINUE
```

Partially unrolling the outer loop inside the inner loop, as shown in loop 46033, has two valuable effects: 1) the vector A(1:N,J) is fetched and stored one-sixth as often as in loop 46031; and 2) giving the compiler more to

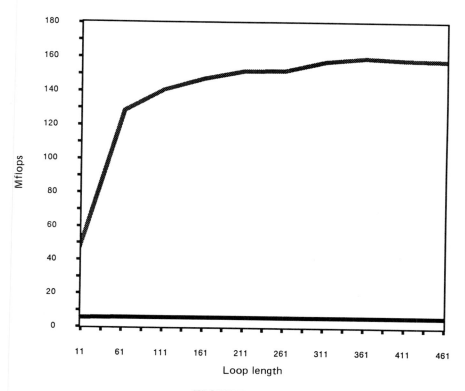

FIGURE 4.32
Performance Comparison of Loops 46020 and 46021, Cray
X-MP. Original, solid line; restructured, dotted line.

do in the inner loop allows overlapped use of more resources. Loop 46034 is
of course a "cleanup" loop that handles N mod 6 remaining iterations.

Another improvement of 50–100% is achieved with this technique
(Figure 4.33). The actual performance of > 150 megaflops is approaching the
kind of performance usually only achieved with hand-coded assembly language routines.

```
          THE RESTRUCTURED
       DO 46032   J = 1, N
         DO 46032 I = 1, N
           A(I,J)=0.
   46032 CONTINUE

       DO 46033    K = 1, N-5, 6
         DO 46033   J = 1, N
           DO 46033 I = 1, N
             A(I,J)  = A(I,J) + B(I,K  ) * C(K  ,J)
       *                      + B(I,K+1) * C(K+1,J)
       *                      + B(I,K+2) * C(K+2,J)
```

```
       *                      + B(I,K+3) * C(K+3,J)
       *                      + B(I,K+4) * C(K+4,J)
       *                      + B(I,K+5) * C(K+5,J)
46033 CONTINUE

      DO 46034  KK = K, N
       DO 46034  J = 1, N
        DO 46034 I = 1, N
         A(I,J) = A(I,J) + B(I,KK) * C(KK ,J)
46034 CONTINUE
```

4.9.8 IF Statements

In DO loops, IF statements can play havoc with optimization. They represent a break in the flow of computation in each iteration, checking to see if something special needs to be done this time through. Testing on the loop index is most offensive, because the answer is already known. A simple restructuring will completely remove the test from the loop.

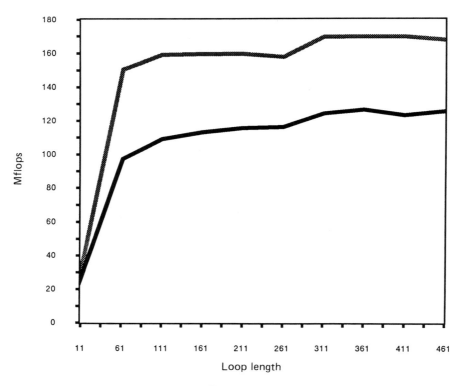

FIGURE 4.33
Performance Comparison of Loops 46031 and 46033–46034,
Cray X-MP. Original, solid line; restructured, dotted line.

Loops 47010, 47011, and 47012 contain tests on the value of the outer loop index, inside the inner loop. The tests are simply causing certain elements of the B and C arrays to be set or not set on every iteration of the inner loop. This is more effectively accomplished by several different loops tailored to each of the special conditions, as shown by loops 47013–47017.

```
C       THE ORIGINAL
        DO 47012   K = 2, N
        DO 47011   J = 2, 3
        DO 47010 I = 2, N
          A(I,J) = (1.   - PX - PY - PZ) * B(I,J,K)
     1             + .5 * PX * ( B(I+1,J,K) + B(I-1,J,K) )
     2             + .5 * PY * ( B(I,J+1,K) + B(I,J-1,K) )
     3             + .5 * PZ * ( B(I,J,K+1) + B(I,J,K-1) )
          IF (K .LT. 3)   GO TO 11
          IF (K .LT. N) GO TO 10
            B(I,J,K )   = A(I,J)
 10         B(I,J,K-1)  = C(I,J)
 11         C(I,J)      = A(I,J)
47010   CONTINUE
47011   CONTINUE
47012 CONTINUE
```

Note that in the original loop nest, the elements of the array A are computed unconditionally. Conditionally computed elements of B feedback to A in the K loop, but never in the I or J loops. This allows us to split out this part of the calculation into the loop nest 47013. Next, we have loop nests 47014 and 47015 computing the values of B and C, depending on the current value of K. And, finally, nest 47017 computes the values for the special case K = N. Performance of the restructured over the original is better than a factor of ten (Figure 4.34).

```
C       THE RESTRUCTURED
        DO 47016   K = 2, N - 1
        DO 47013   J = 2, 3
        DO 47013 I = 2, N
          A(I,J) = (1.   - PX - PY - PZ) * B(I,J,K)
     1             + .5 * PX * ( B(I+1,J,K) + B(I-1,J,K) )
     2             + .5 * PY * ( B(I,J+1,K) + B(I,J-1,K) )
     3             + .5 * PZ * ( B(I,J,K+1) + B(I,J,K-1) )
47013 CONTINUE

        IF (K .EQ. 2) THEN
        DO 47014   J =2, 3
        DO 47014 I =2, N
          C(I,J)    = A(I,J)
47014   CONTINUE
        ELSE
        DO 47015   J = 2, 3
        DO 47015 I = 2, N
          B(I,J,K-1)  = C(I,J)
          C(I,J)      = A(I,J)
47015   CONTINUE
```

```
       ENDIF

47016 CONTINUE

       K = N
       DO 47017  J = 2, 3
         DO 47017  I = 2, N
         A(I,J) = (1.   - PX - PY - PZ) * B(I,J,K)
     1            + .5 * PX * ( B(I+1,J,K) + B(I-1,J,K) )
     2            + .5 * PY * ( B(I,J+1,K) + B(I,J-1,K) )
     3            + .5 * PZ * ( B(I,J,K+1) + B(I,J,K-1) )
         B(I,J,K)    = A(I,J)
         B(I,J,K-1)  = C(I,J)
         C(I,J)      = A(I,J)
47017 CONTINUE
```

Loop nest 47020 contains compound tests on each of the loop indexes, and again, none of these tests need to be in the inner loop. The restructuring

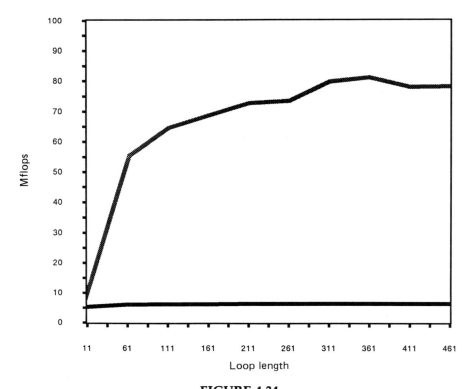

FIGURE 4.34
Performance Comparison of Loops 47012 and 47013 – 47017, Cray X-MP. Original, solid line; restructured, dotted line.

in loops 47021–47029 transforms each of the tests into a series of block IFs
within the J loop, thereby allowing simple vectorization of the I loop.

```
C       THE ORIGINAL
        DO 47020    J = 1, JMAX
        DO 47020    K = 1, KMAX
        DO 47020 I = 1, IMAX
        JP          = J + 1
        JR          = J - 1
        KP          = K + 1
        KR          = K - 1
        IP          = I + 1
        IR          = I - 1

        IF (J .EQ. 1)      GO TO 50
         IF( J .EQ. JMAX) GO TO 51
          XJ = ( A(I,JP,K) - A(I,JR,K) ) * DA2
          YJ = ( B(I,JP,K) - B(I,JR,K) ) * DA2
          ZJ = ( C(I,JP,K) - C(I,JR,K) ) * DA2
          GO TO 70

  50    J1 = J + 1
        J2 = J + 2
        XJ = (-3.  * A(I,J,K) + 4.  * A(I,J1,K) - A(I,J2,K) ) * DA2
        YJ = (-3.  * B(I,J,K) + 4.  * B(I,J1,K) - B(I,J2,K) ) * DA2
        ZJ = (-3.  * C(I,J,K) + 4.  * C(I,J1,K) - C(I,J2,K) ) * DA2
        GO TO 70

  51    J1 = J - 1
        J2 = J - 2
        XJ = ( 3.  * A(I,J,K) - 4.  * A(I,J1,K) + A(I,J2,K) ) * DA2
        YJ = ( 3.  * B(I,J,K) - 4.  * B(I,J1,K) + B(I,J2,K) ) * DA2
        ZJ = ( 3.  * C(I,J,K) - 4.  * C(I,J1,K) + C(I,J2,K) ) * DA2
  70    CONTINUE

        IF (K .EQ. 1)      GO TO 52
         IF (K .EQ. KMAX) GO TO 53
          XK = ( A(I,J,KP) - A(I,J,KR) ) * DB2
          YK = ( B(I,J,KP) - B(I,J,KR) ) * DB2
          ZK = ( C(I,J,KP) - C(I,J,KR) ) * DB2
          GO TO 71

  52    K1 = K + 1
        K2 = K + 2
        XK = (-3.  * A(I,J,K) + 4.  * A(I,J,K1) - A(I,J,K2) ) * DB2
        YK = (-3.  * B(I,J,K) + 4.  * B(I,J,K1) - B(I,J,K2) ) * DB2
        ZK = (-3.  * C(I,J,K) + 4.  * C(I,J,K1) - C(I,J,K2) ) * DB2
        GO TO 71

  53    K1 = K - 1
        K2 = K - 2
        XK = ( 3.  * A(I,J,K) - 4.  * A(I,J,K1) + A(I,J,K2) ) * DB2
        YK = ( 3.  * B(I,J,K) - 4.  * B(I,J,K1) + B(I,J,K2) ) * DB2
        ZK = ( 3.  * C(I,J,K) - 4.  * C(I,J,K1) + C(I,J,K2) ) * DB2
  71    CONTINUE
```

```
            IF (I .EQ. 1)      GO TO 54
            IF (I .EQ. IMAX) GO TO 55
            XI = ( A(IP,J,K) - A(IR,J,K) ) * DC2
            YI = ( B(IP,J,K) - B(IR,J,K) ) * DC2
            ZI = ( C(IP,J,K) - C(IR,J,K) ) * DC2
            GO TO 60

    54      I1 = I + 1
            I2 = I + 2
            XI = (-3.  * A(I,J,K) + 4.  * A(I1,J,K) - A(I2,J,K) ) * DC2
            YI = (-3.  * B(I,J,K) + 4.  * B(I1,J,K) - B(I2,J,K) ) * DC2
            ZI = (-3.  * C(I,J,K) + 4.  * C(I1,J,K) - C(I2,J,K) ) * DC2
            GO TO 60

    55      I1 = I - 1
            I2 = I - 2
            XI = ( 3.  * A(I,J,K) - 4.  * A(I1,J,K) + A(I2,J,K) ) * DC2
            YI = ( 3.  * B(I,J,K) - 4.  * B(I1,J,K) + B(I2,J,K) ) * DC2
            ZI = ( 3.  * C(I,J,K) - 4.  * C(I1,J,K) + C(I2,J,K) ) * DC2
    60      CONTINUE

            DINV     = XJ * YK * ZI  +  YJ * ZK * XI  +  ZJ * XK * YI
        *            - XJ * ZK * YI  -  YJ * XK * ZI  -  ZJ * YK * XI
            D(I,J,K) = 1.  / (DINV + 1.E-51)
  47020 CONTINUE
```

The original loop nest made heavy use of scalar temporaries such as XI, XJ, and XK to carry the conditionally computed values from the top to the bottom of the loop. Since our restructuring splits the original into many loops, we promote the scalars to arrays—such as VAI, VAJ, and VAK—to carry all of the computed values between loops. The transformation may seem drastic, but the flow of control is clearer, the answers are the same, and, as Figure 4.35 illustrates, the performance improvement is astounding; more than a factor of 20 for long vector lengths. Execution time for this loop is dropped from hours to minutes by this technique.

```
    C       THE RESTRUCTURED
            DO 47029 J = 1, JMAX
            DO 47029 K = 1, KMAX

            IF(J.EQ.1)THEN
            J1         = 2
            J2         = 3
            DO 47021 I = 1, IMAX
            VAJ(I) = (-3.  * A(I,J,K) + 4.  * A(I,J1,K) - A(I,J2,K) ) * DA2
            VBJ(I) = (-3.  * B(I,J,K) + 4.  * B(I,J1,K) - B(I,J2,K) ) * DA2
            VCJ(I) = (-3.  * C(I,J,K) + 4.  * C(I,J1,K) - C(I,J2,K) ) * DA2
    47021   CONTINUE

            ELSE IF(J.NE.JMAX) THEN
            JP         = J+1
            JR         = J-1
            DO 47022 I = 1, IMAX
            VAJ(I) = ( A(I,JP,K) - A(I,JR,K) ) * DA2
```

```
          VBJ(I) = ( B(I,JP,K) - B(I,JR,K) ) * DA2
          VCJ(I) = ( C(I,JP,K) - C(I,JR,K) ) * DA2
47022   CONTINUE

        ELSE
        J1          = JMAX-1
        J2          = JMAX-2
        DO 47023 I = 1, IMAX
         VAJ(I) = ( 3.   * A(I,J,K) - 4.   * A(I,J1,K) + A(I,J2,K) ) * DA2
         VBJ(I) = ( 3.   * B(I,J,K) - 4.   * B(I,J1,K) + B(I,J2,K) ) * DA2
         VCJ(I) = ( 3.   * C(I,J,K) - 4.   * C(I,J1,K) + C(I,J2,K) ) * DA2
47023   CONTINUE
        ENDIF

        IF(K.EQ.1) THEN
        K1          = 2
        K2          = 3
        DO 47024 I = 1, IMAX
         VAK(I) = (-3.   * A(I,J,K) + 4.   * A(I,J,K1) - A(I,J,K2) ) * DB2
         VBK(I) = (-3.   * B(I,J,K) + 4.   * B(I,J,K1) - B(I,J,K2) ) * DB2
         VCK(I) = (-3.   * C(I,J,K) + 4.   * C(I,J,K1) - C(I,J,K2) ) * DB2
47024   CONTINUE

        ELSE IF (K.NE.KMAX) THEN
        KP          = K + 1
        KR          = K - 1
        DO 47025 I = 1, IMAX
         VAK(I) = ( A(I,J,KP) - A(I,J,KR) ) * DB2
         VBK(I) = ( B(I,J,KP) - B(I,J,KR) ) * DB2
         VCK(I) = ( C(I,J,KP) - C(I,J,KR) ) * DB2
47025   CONTINUE

        ELSE
        K1          = KMAX - 1
        K2          = KMAX - 2
        DO 47026 I = 1, IMAX
         VAK(I) = ( 3.   * A(I,J,K) - 4.   * A(I,J,K1) + A(I,J,K2) ) * DB2
         VBK(I) = ( 3.   * B(I,J,K) - 4.   * B(I,J,K1) + B(I,J,K2) ) * DB2
         VCK(I) = ( 3.   * C(I,J,K) - 4.   * C(I,J,K1) + C(I,J,K2) ) * DB2
47026   CONTINUE

        I = 1
        I1          = 2
        I2          = 3
        VAI(I) = (-3.   * A(I,J,K) + 4.   * A(I1,J,K) - A(I2,J,K) ) * DC2
        VBI(I) = (-3.   * B(I,J,K) + 4.   * B(I1,J,K) - B(I2,J,K) ) * DC2
        VCI(I) = (-3.   * C(I,J,K) + 4.   * C(I1,J,K) - C(I2,J,K) ) * DC2

        DO 47027 I = 2, IMAX-1
         IP          = I + 1
         IR          = I - 1
         VAI(I) = ( A(IP,J,K) - A(IR,J,K) ) * DC2
         VBI(I) = ( B(IP,J,K) - B(IR,J,K) ) * DC2
         VCI(I) = ( C(IP,J,K) - C(IR,J,K) ) * DC2
47027   CONTINUE
```

```
      I = IMAX
      I1          = IMAX - 1
      I2          = IMAX - 2
      VAI(I) = ( 3.  * A(I,J,K) - 4.  * A(I1,J,K) + A(I2,J,K) ) * DC2
      VBI(I) = ( 3.  * B(I,J,K) - 4.  * B(I1,J,K) + B(I2,J,K) ) * DC2
      VCI(I) = ( 3.  * C(I,J,K) - 4.  * C(I1,J,K) + C(I2,J,K) ) * DC2

      DO 47028 I = 1, IMAX
        DINV = VAJ(I) * VBK(I) * VCI(I) + VBJ(I) * VCK(I) * VAI(I)
     1         + VCJ(I) * VAK(I) * VBI(I) - VAJ(I) * VCK(I) * VBI(I)
     2         - VBJ(I) * VAK(I) * VCI(I) - VCJ(I) * VBK(I) * VAI(I)
        D(I,J,K) = 1.  / (DINV + 1.E-51)
47028 CONTINUE
      ENDIF
47029 CONTINUE
```

Loop 47030 contains three IF tests, only the first of which is actually loop dependent; that is, the value of the logical expression A(I).LT.0.0 can change on each loop iteration, whereas the other two logical expressions are loop independent.

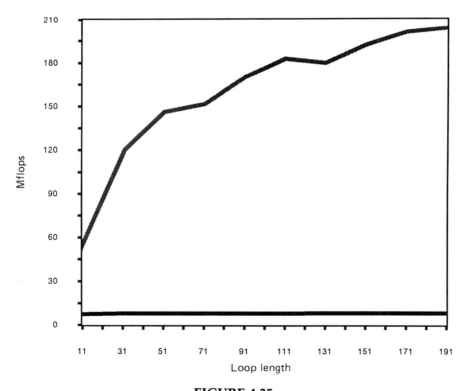

FIGURE 4.35
Performance Comparison of Loops 47020 and 47021–47029,
Cray X-MP. Original, solid line; restructured, dotted line.

A closer examination of the first IF statement reveals that it is just computing the absolute value of the elements of A. The next IF statement (XL.LT.0.) is simply setting certain elements (all, none, even, or odd) of A negative, depending on the value of GAMMA.

```
C       THE ORIGINAL
        DO 47030 I = 1, N
        A(I) = PROD * B(1,I) * A(I)
        IF (A(I) .LT. 0.0) A(I) = -A(I)
        IF (XL .LT. 0.0) A(I) = -A(I)
        IF (GAMMA) 47030, 47030, 100
100     XL = -XL
47030 CONTINUE
```

Our restructuring in loops 47031–47034 simply reflects the analysis in the previous paragraph. Loop 47031 computes the absolute values of the elements of the array A. Then an IF block on the value of GAMMA chooses which (if any) of the elements of A to set negative in the following three loops.

```
C       THE RESTRUCTURED
        DO 47031 I = 1, N
        A(I) = PROD * B(1,I) * A(I)
        A(I) = ABS (A(I))
47031 CONTINUE

        IF (GAMMA .LE. 0.) THEN

        IF (XL .LT. 0.0) THEN
        DO 47032 I = 1, N
        A(I) = -A(I)
47032   CONTINUE
        ENDIF

        ELSE

        IF (XL .LT. 0.0) THEN
        DO 47033 I = 1, N, 2
        A(I) = -A(I)
47033   CONTINUE
        ENDIF

        IF (XL .GT. 0.0) THEN
        DO 47034 I = 2, N, 2
        A(I) = -A(I)
47034   CONTINUE
        ENDIF

        ENDIF
```

As usual, we ignore setting the final value of the scalar XL. If it were needed, the following statement placed after the final ENDIF would properly set it:

```
IF (GAMMA.GT.0.0 .AND. MOD(N,2).EQ.1) XL = -XL
```

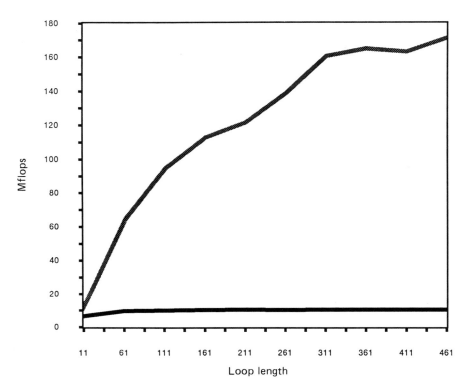

FIGURE 4.36
Performance Comparison of Loops 47030 and 47031–47034,
Cray X-MP. Original, solid line; restructured, dotted line.

Figure 4.36 indicates that the restructured loops run 15 to 20 times faster than the original.

Loop 47050 illustrates the cost of using a computed GO TO to choose among a small number of cases. Loop 47051 is a simple restructuring using a vectorizable IF block to achieve the same results in less than one-tenth of the time, as shown in Figure 4.37.

```
C       THE ORIGINAL
        DO 47050 I = 1, N
        IIA = IA(I)
        GO TO (110, 120) IIA
110     D(I) = B(I)
        A(I) = D(I) + 1.7
        GO TO 47050
120     D(I) = C(I)
        A(I) = D(I) + 1.1
47050 CONTINUE
```

```
C        THE RESTRUCTURED
         DO 47051 I = 1, N
         IF(IA(I) .NE. 2) THEN
           D(I) = B(I)
           A(I) = D(I) + 1.7
         ELSE
           D(I) = C(I)
           A(I) = D(I) + 1.1
         ENDIF
47051 CONTINUE
```

Any time IF blocks are nested within a loop, the probability of executing the inner blocks decreases with each new condition encountered. As the probability or "truth density" decreases, so does the potential vector length within the conditionally executed code blocks. For this reason, all compilers stop trying to vectorize after a certain number of nested IF blocks are en-

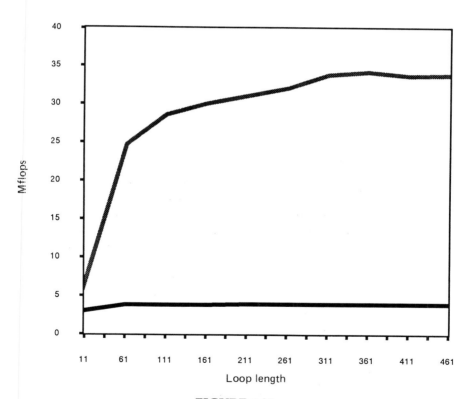

FIGURE 4.37
Performance Comparison of Loops 47050 and 47051, Cray
X-MP. Original, solid line; restructured, dotted line.

countered within a loop. This can be circumvented by reducing all nested blocks to single-level blocks as shown between 47078 and 47079.

```
      DO 47078 I = 1, N
       IF (cond1) THEN
        block1
        IF (cond2) THEN
         block2

        ELSE
         block3
        ENDIF
        block4
       ENDIF
47078 CONTINUE

      DO 47079 I = 1, N
       IF (cond1) THEN
        block1
       ENDIF

       IF (cond1 .AND.  cond2) THEN
        block2
       ENDIF
       IF (cond1 .AND.  .NOT.  cond2) THEN
        block3
       ENDIF

       IF (cond1) THEN
        block4
       ENDIF
47079 CONTINUE
```

The preceding restructuring can (with care) be extended to any number of IF blocks, ELSEIFs, and the like. It can be a valuable tool to clarify *our* thinking about the control flow through the loop, and it may allow us to split out some particularly CPU-intensive block of code. In general, however, the restructuring itself will usually not have any big payoff in performance, even if the restructured loop vectorizes. Loop 47080 is an example of the problems associated with trying to optimize many compounded conditions. No compiler will attempt to vectorize this loop, because of the low probability of executing any of the arithmetic statements following statement 500.

```
C     THE ORIGINAL
      SUM = 0.0
      DO 47080 J = 1, JMAX
      DO 47080 I = 2, N
       IF (I .EQ. N) GO TO 47080
        IF (A(1,J) .LT. B(1,I)) GO TO 47080
         IF (A(1,1) .GT. B(1,I)) GO TO 47080
          IF (A(1,J) .GE. B(1,I+1) .AND.  I .NE. N)  GO TO 500
           IF (J.EQ.1) GO TO 47080
            IF (A(1,J-1) .LT. B(1,I-1) .AND.  I*J .NE. 1)  GO TO 500
             IF (A(1,J-1) .LT. B(1,I)) GO TO 47080
```

```
500     CONTINUE
        P1      = C(1,I-1)
        P2      = D(I-1)
        DD      = B(1,I) - B(1,I-1)
        P3      = (3.0 * E(I) - 2.0 * P2 - D(I)) / DD
        P4      = ( P2 + D(I) - 2.0 * E(I)      ) / DD**2
        SUMND = DD * (P1        + DD * (P2 / 2.
     *          + DD * (P3 / 3. + DD *  P4 / 4.) ) )
        SUM     = SUM + SUMND
47080 CONTINUE
```

Our restructuring in loop 47081 precomputes all of the conditions into one controlling logical variable, LOG7. Note that the very first IF test in the original does nothing but skip the final iteration of the inner loop. This is reflected in the loop limit itself in the restructured code.

All of the arithmetic is done in a simple vectorizable block IF. Figure 4.38 illustrates only a modest performance improvement for this restructuring, because of the very low truth density in the loop; that is, the logical variable LOG7 in the restructured code is true less than 2% of the time, resulting in extremely short vector lengths.

```
C       THE RESTRUCTURED
        SUM = 0.0
        DO 47081 J = 1, JMAX
        DO 47081 I = 2, N-1

        LOG1 = A(1,J) .GE. B(1,I)
        LOG2 = A(1,1) .LE. B(1,I)
        LOG3 = A(1,J) .GE. B(1,I+1)
        LOG4 = J .NE. 1
        LOG5 = A(1,J-1) .LT. B(1,I-1)
        LOG6 = A(1,J-1) .GE. B(1,I)
        LOG7 = LOG1 .AND.  LOG2 .AND.  LOG3 .OR.
     *         LOG1 .AND.  LOG2 .AND.  LOG4 .AND.  LOG5 .OR.
     *         LOG1 .AND.  LOG2 .AND.  LOG4 .AND.  LOG6

        P1      = C(1,I-1)
        P2      = D(I-1)
        DD      = B(1,I) - B(1,I-1)
        IF ( .NOT. LOG7) DD = 1.0
        P3      = (3.0 * E(I) - 2.0 * P2 - D(I)) / DD
        P4      = ( P2 + D(I) - 2.0 * E(I)      ) / DD**2
        SUMND = 0.0
        IF (LOG7) SUMND = DD * (P1        + DD * (P2 / 2.
     *                    + DD * (P3 / 3. + DD *  P4 / 4.) ) )
        SUM     = SUM + SUMND
47081 CONTINUE
```

Loop 47090 is a renumbered version of kernel 15 of the Livermore Fortran kernels. At this time (February 1988) only a few compilers have demonstrated an ability to vectorize this loop. It is a jumble of arithmetic IF tests and unconditional GO TOs. Yet if the conditional blocks are sorted out and more clearly expressed as block IFs, almost any compiler can vectorize it.

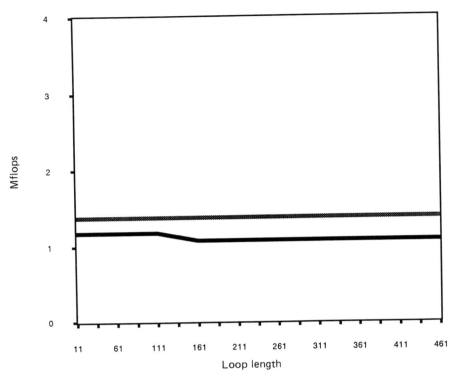

FIGURE 4.38
Performance Comparison of Loops 47080 and 47081, Cray
X-MP. Original, solid line; restructured, dotted line.

Loops 47091–47093 are such a restructuring, and Figure 4.39 depicts about a
factor of eight performance improvement over the original.

```
C      THE ORIGINAL
   15 DO 47090  J = 2, NR
      DO 47090  K = 2, NZ
            IF (J - NR) 31, 30, 30
   30    VY(K,J) = 0.0
            GO TO 47090
   31       IF( VH(K,J+1) - VH(K,J)) 33, 33, 32
   32       T = AR
            GO TO 34
   33       T = BR
   34    IF (VF(K,J) - VF(K-1,J)) 35, 36, 36
   35       R = AMAX1 (VH(K-1,J), VH(K-1,J+1))
            S = VF(K-1,J)
            GO TO 37
   36       R = AMAX1 (VH(K,J), VH(K,J+1))
            S = VF(K,J)
   37    VY(K,J) = SQRT (VG(K,J)**2 + R*R) * T / S
```

```
   38              IF (K - NZ) 40, 39, 39
   39      VS(K,J) = 0.
                    GO TO 47090
   40              IF (VF(K,J) - VF(K,J-1)) 41, 42, 42
   41                R = AMAX1 (VG(K,J-1), VG(K+1,J-1))
                     S = VF(K,J-1)
                     T = BR
                     GO TO 43
   42                R = AMAX1 (VG(K,J), VG(K+1,J))
                     S = VF(K,J)
                     T = AR
   43      VS(K,J) = SQRT (VH(K,J)**2 + R*R) * T / S
47090 CONTINUE
C     THE RESTRUCTURED
      DO 47091  J = 2, NR-1
      DO 47091  K = 2, NZ-1

        IF (VH(K,J+1) .GT. VH(K,J)) THEN
         T = AR
        ELSE
         T = BR
        ENDIF

        IF (VF(K,J) .LT. VF(K-1,J)) THEN
         R = AMAX1 (VH(K-1,J), VH(K-1,J+1))
         S = VF(K-1,J)
        ELSE
         R = AMAX1 (VH(K,J), VH(K,J+1))
         S = VF(K,J)
        ENDIF

        VY(K,J) = SQRT (VG(K,J)**2 + R*R) * T / S

        IF (VF(K,J) .LT. VF(K,J-1)) THEN
         R = AMAX1 (VG(K,J-1), VG(K+1,J-1))
         S = VF(K,J-1)
         T = BR
        ELSE
         R = AMAX1 (VG(K,J), VG(K+1,J))
         S = VF(K,J)
         T = AR
        ENDIF

        VS(K,J) = SQRT (VH(K,J)**2 + R*R) * T / S
47091 CONTINUE

      DO 47092 J = 2, NR-1
       VS(NZ,J) = 0.
47092 CONTINUE

      DO 47093  K = 2, NZ
       VY(K,NR) = 0.0
47093 CONTINUE
```

Loops 47100 and 47101 represent a conventionally coded table lookup and interpolation scheme. In this example we do N table searches, interpo-

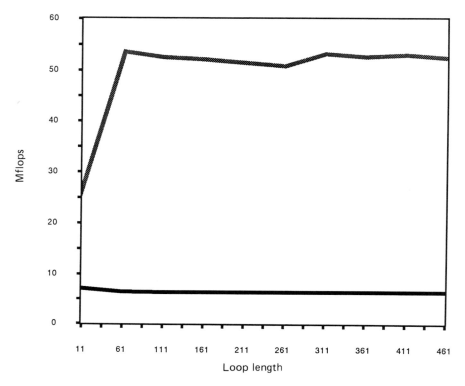

FIGURE 4.39

Performance Comparison of Loops 47090 and 47091–47093,
Cray X-MP. Original, solid line; restructured, dotted line.

lating for each of the input values X2(I). The inner loop (47100) is very
difficult to vectorize because of the jump out of loop (GO TO 21) and also
because the index IL must be carried on to the interpolation for Y2(I).

```
C       THE ORIGINAL
        DO 47101 I = 1, N
        U1 = X2(I)

        DO 47100 LT = 1, NTAB
         IF (U1 .GT. X1(LT)) GO TO 47100
          IL = LT
          GO TO 121
47100  CONTINUE

        IL = NTAB - 1
121     Y2(I) = Y1(IL) + ( Y1(IL+1) - Y1(IL) ) /
       *                 ( X1(IL+1) - X1(IL) ) *
       *                 ( X2(I)  - X1(IL) )
47101  CONTINUE
```

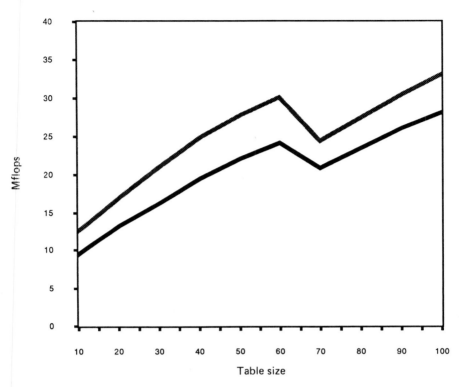

FIGURE 4.40
Performance Comparison of Loops 47101 and 47102 – 47104,
Cray X-MP. Original, solid line; restructured, dotted line.

Our approach to restructuring this loop is to split the table lookup and interpolation into separate loops, thereby allowing the important interpolation arithmetic to vectorize. We promote IL to the array IV and compute all of the interpolation indexes in loop 47103, which can then vectorize even with th? jump out of loop. These indexes are then used in loop 47104 to provide indirect address vectorization of the interpolation. Figure 4.40 presents the performance graphed against various table lengths for given N = 461. As before, the sharp dip in performance between 60 and 70 results from the Cray vector-register length of 64.

```
C       THE RESTRUCTURED
        DO 47103 I = 1, N
        U1 = X2(I)

        DO 47102 LT = 1, NTAB
        IF (U1 .GT. X1(LT)) GO TO 47102
        IV(I) = LT
        GO TO 47103
47102   CONTINUE
```

```
          IV(I) = NTAB - 1
47103 CONTINUE

      DO 47104 I  =  1, N
        Y2(I) = Y1(IV(I)) + ( Y1(IV(I)+1) - Y1(IV(I)) ) /
     *                      ( X1(IV(I)+1) - X1(IV(I)) ) *
     *                      ( X2(I) - X1(IV(I)) )
47104 CONTINUE
```

Loop 47102 is simple enough to allow some compilers to vectorize it using special library functions. As a general rule, however, a loop that contains a jump out of loop, such as 47110, cannot be easily vectorized, since loop termination (vector length) cannot be determined.

```
      DO 47110 I = 1, N
        A(I) = B(I) * SQRT (D(I)) - C(I)
        IF (A(I) .LT. 0.) GO TO 47111
              . . .
        vectorizable code block
        (running in scalar because of jump out of loop)
              . . .
47110 CONTINUE
              . . .
47111 CONTINUE
```

Given that ITERM is the value of I when the loop exit is taken, then a restructuring technique that usually has a payoff for large ITERM is stripmining. This involves performing the loop in "strips," typically an integer multiple of the size of the vector registers on the target machine. Such a restructuring for a Cray machine is shown in loop 47112.

```
      DIMENSION TEMPA(64)
          . . .
      DO 47112 II = 1, N, 64
       LENGTH = MIN (64, N-I+1)

       I = II - 1
       DO 47113 J = 1, LENGTH
        I = I + 1
        TEMPA(J) = B(I) * SQRT (D(I)) - C(I)
47113  CONTINUE

       I = II - 1
       DO 47114 JJ = 1, LENGTH
        I = I + 1
        A(I) = TEMPA(JJ)
        IF (A(I) .LT. 0.) GO TO 47115
47114  CONTINUE
47115  CONTINUE

       JJ = JJ - 1
       DO 47116 I = II, II+JJ-1
        vectorizable code block
47116  CONTINUE
```

```
        IF (JJ .LT. LENGTH) GO TO 47117
47112 CONTINUE
47117 CONTINUE
```

It should be obvious that such a technique must be applied with care. It is a significant transformation of the original loop but can have a sizable payoff for a large, CPU-intensive loop. Let us step through the transformation. First, vectorize the computation of the elements of the array A (47113) and isolate the vectorizable code block into a loop by itself (47116). This is achieved by computing the elements 64 at a time in a temporary array (47113). Then set the next 64 array elements and check for loop termination within that group (47114). Compute the vectorizable code block for just those iterations in which A(I) .GE. 0. (47116); and, finally, exit the loop when the termination condition has been satisfied.

Note that here we have used our knowledge that if loop 47114 terminates normally, then JJ = LENGTH+1; for exit via the GO TO statement, JJ will be less than or equal to LENGTH. Our next example, loop 47120 is a simple IF loop, which harks back to the earliest days of Fortran, Before DO Loops (BDL). A few compilers recognize such loops, but most do not. Our restructuring in loop 47121 is a simple transformation, and performance increases by more than a factor of ten (Figure 4.41).

```
C       THE ORIGINAL
        I = 0
47120 CONTINUE
        I = I + 1
        A(I) = B(I)**2 + .5 * C(I) * D(I) / E(I)
        IF (I .LT. N) GO TO 47120

C       THE RESTRUCTURED
        DO 47121 I = 1, N
        A(I) = B(I)**2 + .5 * C(I) * D(I) / E(I)
47121 CONTINUE
```

Loop 47130 is not a simple IF loop, but a loop with an indeterminate termination based on the criterion (A(I).GT.0), which, if the algorithm is ill conditioned, has the potential to never be false—resulting in an infinite loop. Such loops are common on systems that do not have a "DO WHILE" extension to the language. Even with the extension such a loop is difficult for a compiler to vectorize, since the final value to be computed remains indeterminate.

```
C       THE ORIGINAL
        I = 0
47130 CONTINUE
        I = I + 1
        A(I) = B(I)**2 + .5 * C(I) * D(I) / E(I)
        IF (A(I) .GT. 0.) GO TO 47130
```

Our approach here is to stripmine the loop the same as we did in our previous example of a jump out of a loop. We compute the next 128 values

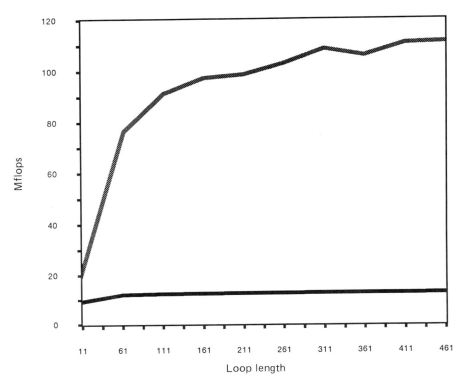

FIGURE 4.41
Performance Comparison of Loops 47120 and 47121, Cray
X-MP. Original, solid line; restructured, dotted line.

into a temporary array VA with full vectorization in loop 47131, then test for
convergence in loop 47132. Performance depends on the point at which
convergence occurs; as more and more elements of A are computed, the
performance of the restructured code improves, whereas performance of the
original is relatively flat, and, for early convergence, actually outperforms the
restructured (Figure 4.42).

Using this technique always requires experimentation to determine
whether the nature of our algorithm lends itself to stripmining.

```
C       THE RESTRUCTURED
        DO 47133 II = 1, N, 128
        LENGTH = MINO (128, N-II+1)
        DO 47131 I = 1, LENGTH
           VA(I) = B(I+II-1)**2 + .5 * C(I+II-1) * D(I+II-1) / E(I+II-1)
47131   CONTINUE

        DO 47132 I = 1, LENGTH
        A(I+II-1) = VA(I)
        IF (A(I+II-1) .LE. 0.0) GO TO 47134
```

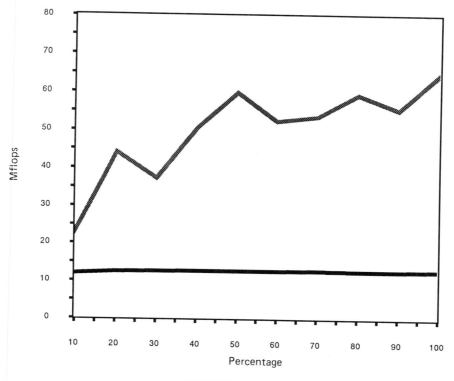

FIGURE 4.42
Performance Comparison of Loops 47130 and 47131–47133,
Cray X-MP. Original, solid line; restructured, dotted line.

```
47132  CONTINUE
47133  CONTINUE
47134  CONTINUE
```

Our final example is another of the Livermore kernels, Number 17. Our restructuring performs no differently than the original, because of the recursive nature of several of the scalar variables, such as XNM and E6. We present the restructuring simply to illustrate that a side benefit of the effort to vectorize is often a loop that more clearly states the algorithm. We believe that loop 47143 is much easier to follow and more easily maintained than the original loops 47140 and 47141. Figure 4.43 presents the performance of the original and the restructured loops.

```
C       THE ORIGINAL
              I  = N
              J  = 1
            INK  = -1
          SCALE  = 5./3.
            XNM  = 1./3.
             E6  = 1.03/3.07
                GO TO 47141
```

```
C                                                STEP MODEL
47140           E6 = XNM * VSP(I) + VSTP(I)
          VXNE(I) = E6
              XNM = E6
          VE3(I) = E6
                I = I + INK
                IF (I .EQ. J) GO TO  47142
47141           E3 = XNM * VLR(I) + VLIN(I)
             XNEI = VXNE(I)
          VXND(I) = E6
              XNC = SCALE * E3
C                                              SELECT MODEL
          IF ( XNM  .GT. XNC) GO TO  47140
          IF ( XNEI .GT. XNC) GO TO  47140
C                                              LINEAR MODEL
          VE3(I) = E3
              E6 = E3 + E3 - XNM
         VXNE(I) = E3 + E3 - XNEI
             XNM = E6
               I = I + INK
               IF (I .NE. J) GO TO 47141
47142 CONTINUE

C     THE RESTRUCTURED
             XNM = 1./3.
              E6 = 1.03/3.07
      DO 47143 I = N, 2, -1
      E3       = XNM * VLR(I) + VLIN(I)
      XNEI     = VXNE(I)
      VXND(I)  = E6
      XNC      = SCALE * E3
      IF (XNM .LE. XNC .AND.  XNEI .LE. XNC) THEN
        VE3(I)   = E3
        E6       = E3 + E3 - XNM
        VXNE(I)  = E3 + E3 - XNEI
        XNM      = E6
      ELSE
        E6       = XNM * VSP(I) + VSTP(I)
        VXNE(I)  = E6
        XNM      = E6
        VE3(I)   = E6
      ENDIF
47143 CONTINUE
```

4.9.9 Subprogram References

Subroutine calls and external (user) function references in a DO loop play havoc with optimization and prevent vectorization of the loop. Compilers handle only one subprogram at a time and so can know nothing about the use of program variables in an external routine. So when a subprogram reference is encountered in a loop, the compiler must save in memory all needed registers as well as the current values of any variables. It does so on the assumption that not only will the subprogram destroy all register con-

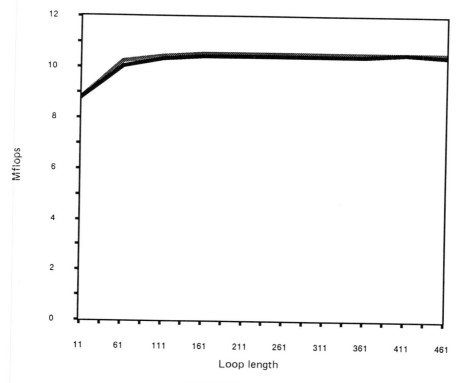

FIGURE 4.43
Performance Comparison of Loops 47140–47141 and 47143,
Cray X-MP. Original, solid line; restructured, dotted line.

tents, but might also contain recursive references to program variables. The only exceptions to this are references to some Fortran-intrinsic functions and certain machine-specific library functions known to the compiler.

We will explore optimizing such loops with the following techniques:

1. Splitting the loop to isolate the external reference into a loop of its own

2. Replacing an external function definition with a statement function

3. Pulling the code of the external routine into the referencing loop

4. Pushing the loop into the subprogram

5. Restructuring a scalar function into a vector subroutine

Subprograms that can be safely split out of a calling loop satisfy the following conditions.

1. The subprogram has no side effects on the calling loop; that is, it makes no assignments to variables or arrays being referenced in the loop.

2. The subprogram contains no STOP statements or alternate RETURNs.

3. The subprogram dummy arguments corresponding to actual arguments that are array elements are specified as variable names, not arrays.

4. If the subprogram references other nonintrinsic subprograms, then these subprograms satisfy the preceding three conditions, as well as this one.

Our first example in loop 48010 will not vectorize, because a compiler does not know whether FRED has any side effects within the loop. We have included a listing of FRED so that the reader may verify that FRED neither references or sets any external variables. It simply returns a value computed as a function of its input argument. As a result, we may split the reference to FRED into a separate loop, thereby allowing all the rest of the arithmetic to vectorize. This is shown in loops 48011–48013.

```
C       THE ORIGINAL
        DO 48010 I = 1, N
        A(I) = B(I) * C(I)
        D(I) = FRED (A(I)**2 + 2.0)
        E(I) = D(I) / B(I) + A(I)
48010 CONTINUE

        FUNCTION FRED (X)
        DATA C0, C1, C2, C3, C4, C5, C6, C7, C8, C9
      *   / .1, .2, .3, .4, .5, .6, .7, .8, .9, 1. /

        FRED = C0 + X * (C1 + X * (C2 + X * (C3
      *            + X * (C4 + X * (C5 + X * (C6
      *            + X * (C7 + X * (C8 + X * (C9 + X))))))))))

        RETURN
        END
```

Note that the original argument to FRED was the vectorizable expression $A(I)**2 + 2.0$. To vectorize the expression, we use the array D to carry the values from loop 48011 to 48012. Since the value of FRED is unconditionally stored into D(I) in loop 48012, there is no problem with using D in this manner.

```
C       THE RESTRUCTURED
        DO 48011 I = 1,N
        A(I) = B(I) * C(I)
        D(I) = A(I)**2 + 2.0
48011 CONTINUE
```

```
      DO 48012 I = 1,N
         D(I) = FRED (D(I))
48012 CONTINUE

      DO 48013 I = 1,N
         E(I) = D(I) / B(I) + A(I)
48013 CONTINUE
```

Figure 4.44 indicates about a 25% performance improvement for this restructuring. If FRED were less CPU intensive and the 48010 loop more complicated, the improvement could be as much as a factor of ten.

Loop 48020 contains another function reference, FUNC, and again, it is stopping vectorization of the loop. Remember, this could be embedded in a much longer loop, and a compiler would not be able to vectorize any of the code for fear of side effects from FUNC. Once more we have listed the contents of FUNC, and in reality the system probably spends more time calling the routine than it does executing the code.

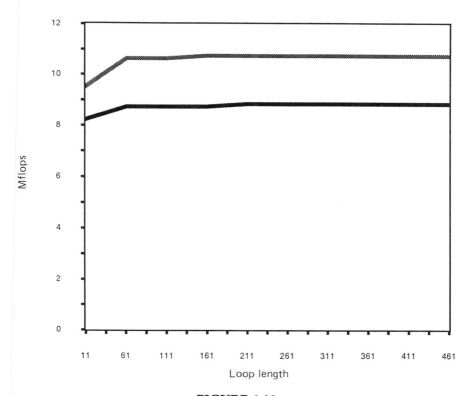

FIGURE 4.44

Performance Comparison of Loops 48010 and 48011–48013,
Cray X-MP. Original, solid line; restructured, dotted line.

```
C       THE ORIGINAL
        DO 48020 I = 1, N
        A(I) = B(I) * FUNC (D(I)) + C(I)
48020 CONTINUE

        FUNCTION FUNC (X)
        FUNC = X**2 + 2.0 / X
        RETURN
        END
```

Our restructuring simply brings the function definition into the routine with a statement function. A compiler will expand this definition in line and vectorize the resultant code. Even on this little loop, it should be clear that calling the external function is quite costly, since Figure 4.45 indicates a performance improvement of more than a factor of 20 for long vectors: An hour of CPU time is reduced to less than three minutes.

```
C       THE RESTRUCTURED
        FUNCX (X) = X**2 + 2.0 / X
            . . .
        DO 48021 I = 1, N
        A(I) = B(I) * FUNCX (D(I)) + C(I)
48021 CONTINUE
```

Since our goal is to vectorize as much code as possible, pulling the external code into the loop is a good place to start. Consider loop 48030 and the code of external routine SSUB.

```
        DO 48030 I = 1, N
        X(I) = SQRT (Y(I)**2 + Z(I)**2)
        ZT = PI * X(I) + COS(A(I))
        CALL SSUB ( X(I), ZT, TY(I), TZ(I) )
        TX(I) = ABS (TZ(I))**0.5
48030 CONTINUE

        SUBROUTINE SSUB (Y1, Y2, Y3, Y4)
        Y4 = Y1**2 + ALOG (ABS (Y1 + Y2))
     *             * EXP (Y2 * ABS (Y1 - Y2))
        Y3 = Y1 + Y2
        RETURN
        END
```

To begin, we will substitute the code from SSUB into loop 48030, creating loop 48031.

```
        DO 48031 I = 1, N
        X(I) = SQRT (Y(I)**2 + Z(I)**2)
        ZT = PI * X(I) + COS(A(I))
        TZ(I) = X(I)**2 + ALOG (ABS (X(I) + ZT))
     *               * EXP (ZT * ABS ( X(I) - ZT))
        TY(I) = X(I) + ZT
        TX(I) = ABS (TZ(I))**0.5
48031 CONTINUE
```

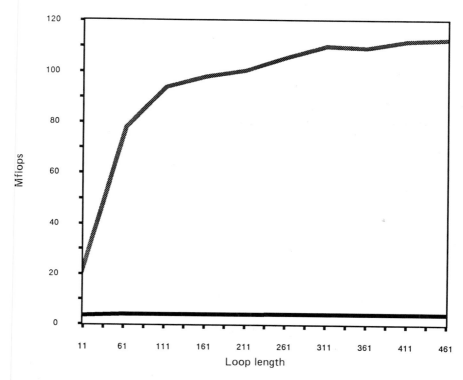

FIGURE 4.45

Performance Comparison of Loops 48020 and 48021, Cray
X-MP. Original, solid line; restructured, dotted line.

Inspection of this loop reveals no recursion. Therefore, it will vectorize
as written, assuming that each of the intrinsic functions has a vector version.
Not only do vector instructions replace unoptimized scalar instructions, but
N subroutine calls have been eliminated, another performance boost. But
eliminating subroutine calls is often a maintenance headache. In how many
other places is SSUB called? Should they each be changed in this manner?
What if changes are made to SSUB in the future; will the programmer
remember to make corresponding changes in loop 48031? The answers to
these questions usually argue against this approach.

As an alternative, can we split the subroutine call out of the loop and
achieve the same level of performance improvement? In other words, will
loops 48032, 48033, and 48034 produce the same answers as did 48030 and
with the same degree of efficiency as 48031?

```
      DO 48032 I = 1, N
        X(I) = SQRT (Y(I)**2 + Z(I)**2)
        ZT = PI * X(I) + COS(A(I))
48032 CONTINUE
```

```
      DO 48033 I = 1, N
      CALL SSUB ( X(I), ZT, TY(I), TZ(I) )
48033 CONTINUE

      DO 48034 I = 1, N
      TX(I) = ABS (TZ(I))**0.5
48034 CONTINUE
```

The answer to both questions is "no." In the original loop, ZT assumed a sequence of values, each of which was passed to SSUB. Now only the last value of ZT is passed in each CALL. Furthermore, the code inside SSUB is very CPU intensive, and it is still being computed in scalar mode.

The first problem is easy to address by promoting ZT to an array, as shown in loops 48042, 48043, and 48044.

```
      DO 48042 I = 1, N
      X(I) = SQRT (Y(I)**2 + Z(I)**2)
      VZT(I) = PI * X(I) + COS(A(I))
48042 CONTINUE

      DO 48043 I = 1, N
      CALL SSUB ( X(I), VZT(I), TY(I), TZ(I) )
48043 CONTINUE

      DO 48044 I = 1, N
      TX(I) = ABS (TZ(I))**0.5
48044 CONTINUE
```

Next, we can create a new version of SSUB, named VSSUB, by pushing the loop into SSUB and passing whole arrays as arguments, as shown in loops 48052, 48053, and 48054.

```
      DO 48052 I = 1, N
      X(I) = SQRT (Y(I)**2 + Z(I)**2)
      VZT(I) = PI * X(I) + COS(A(I))
48052 CONTINUE

      ZT = VZT(N)
      CALL VSSUB (N, X, VZT, TY, TZ )

      DO 48054 I = 1, N
      TX(I) = ABS (TZ(I))**0.5
48054 CONTINUE

      SUBROUTINE VSSUB (N, Y1, Y2, Y3, Y4)
      DIMENSION Y1(*), Y2(*), Y3(*), Y4(*)
Comment: Changes made to this routine necessitate changes to SSUB.
      DO 48053 I = 1, N
      Y4(I) = Y1(I)**2 + ALOG (ABS (Y1(I) + Y2(I)))
     *            * EXP (Y2(I) * ABS (Y1(I) - Y2(I)))
      Y3(I) = Y1(I) + Y2(I)
48053 CONTINUE
      RETURN
      END
```

This restructuring allows all of the original code to vectorize and reduces the number of subroutine calls from N down to one. The overall
performance is very close to that of 48031, and maintenance is manageable
with comments in both SSUB and VSSUB (shown). Such a transformation is
relatively easy to perform with an editor. For this example, all that was
needed was to

- Add the DO loop length N to both the actual and dummy argument
  lists. Replace the actual array element arguments with the array
  names.

- Dimension the dummy arguments.

- Place a DO loop around the original scalar code.

- Add the subscript expression (I) to each reference to a dummy argument.

- Save the last value of VZT(N) into the original scalar ZT.

Loop 48060 contains yet another function call, and here we introduce a
few more twists. A careful reading of UFUN will reveal that its reference can
be split out into a loop of its own, just as we did with FRED in loop 48010.
But this loop also contains the scalar temporary AOLD that carries a value
from the first line of the loop into each of the other statements. So to split the
loop we must promote AOLD to be an array of values VAOLD.

Now to go one step further than we did with FRED: We push the loop
into the function. To do this, we transform the scalar function UFUN into a
vector *subroutine* VUFUN. This is accomplished by: 1) adding the DO loop
length N to the argument list; 2) changing the loop-dependent scalar argument AOLD to the array of arguments VAOLD; 3) changing the array
element argument B(I) to the array argument B; 4) adding the actual argument A to the call and the corresponding dummy argument UFUN to the
subroutine statement; 5) naming the new routine VUFUN; 6) dimensioning
the promoted arrays X, Y, and UFUN; and 7) noting that the statement IF
(SCA.GT.1.0) is loop independent, we add vectorizable DO loops 10 and 20
to compute all of the values of UFUN before returning to the calling routine.

In Figure 4.46, this restructuring—which is easy to carry out with an
editor—results in a performance improvement of better than a factor of
twenty.

```
C      THE ORIGINAL
       DO 48060 I = 1, N
       AOLD = A(I)
       A(I) = UFUN (AOLD, B(I), SCA)
       C(I) = (A(I) + AOLD) * .5
48060 CONTINUE
```

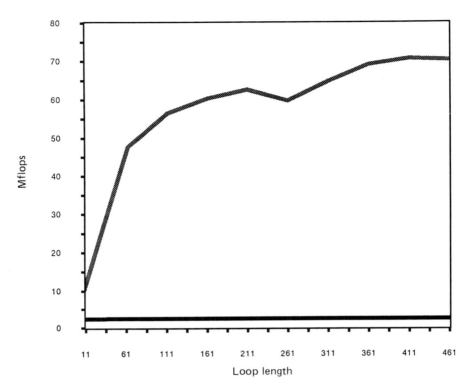

FIGURE 4.46
Performance Comparison of Loops 48060 and 48061–48062,
Cray X-MP. Original, solid line; restructured, dotted line.

```
        FUNCTION UFUN (X, Y, SCA)
        IF (SCA .GT. 1.0) GO TO 10
        UFUN = SQRT (X**2 + Y**2)
        GO TO 5
10      UFUN = 0.0
5       CONTINUE
        RETURN
        END


C       THE RESTRUCTURED
        DO 48061 I = 1, N
        VAOLD(I) = A(I)
48061 CONTINUE

        CALL VUFUN (N, VAOLD, B, SCA, A)

        DO 48062 I = 1, N
        C(I) = (A(I) + VAOLD(I)) * .5
48062 CONTINUE
```

```
      SUBROUTINE VUFUN (N, X, Y, SCA, UFUN)
      DIMENSION X(*), Y(*), UFUN(*)
      IF (SCA .GT. 1.0) GO TO 15
         DO 10 I = 1, N
         UFUN(I) = SQRT (X(I)**2 + Y(I)**2)
   10 CONTINUE
      RETURN
   15 CONTINUE
         DO 20 I = 1, N
         UFUN(I) = 0.0
   20 CONTINUE
      RETURN
      END
```

In loop 48070, vectorization is of course prevented by the call to SSUB. As in the preceding examples, SSUB has no side effects on the loop. Rather than pushing the loop into the subroutine, however, we expand the code into the loop by substituting the actual arguments in line in loop 48071. This eliminates N subroutine calls and allows all of the operations to be performed with vector instructions.

The performance improvement of about a factor of 20 shown in Figure 4.47 is similar to that of "loop pushing" in the previous example. We tend to prefer the loop-pushing technique because it retains code modularity. If in-loop expansion is carried to an extreme, a program can become monolithic.

```
C        THE ORIGINAL
         DO 48070 I = 1, N
         A(I) = (B(I)**2 + C(I)**2)
         CT   = PI * A(I) + (A(I))**2
         CALL SSUB (A(I), CT, D(I), E(I))
         F(I) = (ABS (E(I)))
48070 CONTINUE

      SUBROUTINE SSUB (Y1, Y2, Y3, Y4)
      Y4 = Y1**2 + (ABS (Y1 + Y2)) * (Y2 * ABS (Y1 - Y2))
      Y3 = Y1 + Y2
      RETURN
      END

C        THE RESTRUCTURED
         DO 48071 I = 1, N
         A(I) = (B(I)**2 + C(I)**2)
         CT   = PI * A(I) + (A(I))**2
         E(I) = A(I)**2 + (ABS (A(I) + CT)) * (CT * ABS (A(I) - CT))
         D(I) = A(I) + CT
         F(I) = (ABS (E(I)))
48071 CONTINUE
```

Now let us add some complications to the original loop (48030) and examine how they affect our ability to restructure for vectorization. The additions involve the scalars SCA1 and SCA2, the array TX, and the loop index I. We offset them in loop 48078 and in SSUB1 to highlight them.

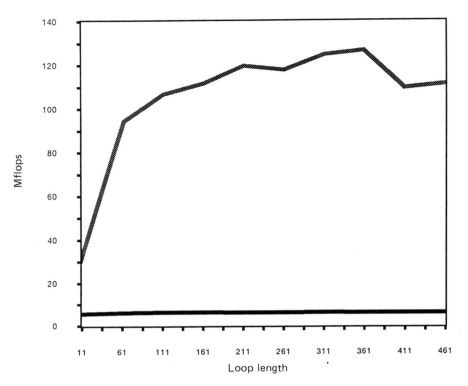

FIGURE 4.47

Performance Comparison of Loops 48070 and 48071, Cray
X-MP. Original, solid line; restructured, dotted line.

```
        COMMON /SCALAR/ SCA1, I
        COMMON /VECTOR/ TX(100)
              . . .
     DO 48078 I = 1, N
        X(I) = SQRT (Y(I)**2 + Z(I)**2)      + SCA1
        ZT = PI * X(I) + COS(A(I))
        CALL SSUB1 ( X(I), ZT, TY(I), TZ(I),     SCA2 )
        TX(I) = ABS (TZ(I))**0.5
           SCA2 = TX(I) * ZT
48078 CONTINUE

     SUBROUTINE SSUB1 (Y1, Y2, Y3, Y4,     Y5)
        COMMON /SCALAR/ SCA1, I
        COMMON /VECTOR/ TX(100)
              . . .
     Y4 = Y1**2 + ALOG (ABS (Y1 + Y2))
     *          * EXP (Y2 * ABS (Y1 - Y2))
     Y3 = Y1 + Y2        * TX (I-1)
           SCA1 = Y1 * Y2 + Y5
     RETURN
     END
```

It is usually straightforward to pull subroutine code into a DO loop, so we begin by doing that to examine the loop for recursive data dependencies. This is shown in loop 48079.

```
        COMMON /SCALAR/ SCA1, I
        COMMON /VECTOR/ TX(100)
             . . .
     DO 48079 I = 1, N
       X(I) = SQRT (Y(I)**2 + Z(I)**2)        + SCA1
       ZT = PI * X(I) + COS(A(I))
       TZ(I) = X(I)**2 + ALOG (ABS (X(I) + ZT))
   *                   * EXP (ZT * ABS ( X(I) - ZT))
       TY(I) = X(I) + ZT          * TX(I-1)
          SCA1 = X(I) * ZT + SCA2
       TX(I) = ABS (TZ(I))**0.5
          SCA2 = TX(I) * ZT
 48079 CONTINUE
```

Three recursive relationships have been uncovered here in the introduced code: SCA1 and SCA2 are both wrap-around scalars. That is, they are each referenced before being set; and TX(I−1) is referenced before TX(I) is set. It should be clear that the loop cannot vectorize as written. In the interest of retaining program modularity we would prefer to split out the original subroutine call and push the loop into it. But can we do that? In general, loops cannot be split if recursion crosses the proposed loop boundaries and, in this case, if recursion crosses the subroutine boundary. The recursiveness revealed in loop 48079 tells us that splitting the CALL out of the original loop would generate wrong answers.

By pulling the subroutine code into the calling loop we have revealed three different ways recursion can arise across subprogram boundaries: 1) through scalars passed in COMMON (SCA1); 2) through scalars passed on the argument list (SCA2); and 3) through array references with different indexes (TX(I), and TX(I−1)). In general these conditions introduce severe difficulties in optimizing the code. Loop 48080 is fabricated to show the handling of problems associated with scalar variables being shared among a calling routine and two subroutines called from within a loop. We admit that this code is mostly nonsensical in its shortness, but it represents interactions that happen in real-world code.

The scalar SCA is passed to SUB1 where it is set, then returned. It is sent again to SUB2 where it is set once more, then returned to take part in the calculation of D(I). SUB1 and SUB2 also share the variable SCALR through a common block.

```
 C      THE ORIGINAL
        DO 48080 I = 1, N
        A(I) = SQRT (B(I)**2 + C(I)**2)
        CALL SUB1 (A(I), B(I), SCA)
        CALL SUB2 (SCA)
        D(I) = SQRT (ABS (A(I) + SCA) )
 48080 CONTINUE
```

```
SUBROUTINE SUB1 (X, Y, SCA)
COMMON /SCALAR/ SCALR
SCA = X**2 + Y**2
SCALR = SCA * 2
RETURN
END

SUBROUTINE SUB2 (SCA)
COMMON /SCALAR/ SCALR
SCA = SCA + SCALR
RETURN
END
```

Our restructuring promotes both SCA and SCALR to arrays, splits the subroutine calls out of the loop, and pushes the loop into each, renaming them VSUB1 and VSUB2. The vector VSCA now carries all of the values of the original SCA among the loops 48081 and 48082 and both routines. The common variable SCALR is properly set at the end of the new routine VSUB1. As in previous examples we do not bother to save the last value of the local scalar SCA, although if it were necessary it would be easy to do.

As with other examples in this section, Figure 4.48 shows about a factor of 20 improvement from the original loop to the restructured.

```
C      THE RESTRUCTURED
       DO 48081 I = 1, N
         A(I) = SQRT (B(I)**2 + C(I)**2)
48081 CONTINUE

       CALL VSUB1 (N, A, B, VSCA, VSCALR)

       CALL VSUB2 (N, VSCA, VSCALR)

       DO 48082 I = 1, N
         D(I) = SQRT (ABS (A(I) + VSCA(I) ) )
48082 CONTINUE

       SUBROUTINE VSUB1 (N, X, Y, SCA, VSCALR)
       DIMENSION X(*), Y(*), SCA(*), VSCALR(*)
       COMMON /SCALAR/ SCALR
       DO 10 I = 1, N
         SCA(I) = X(I)**2 +Y(I)**2
         VSCALR(I) = SCA(I) * 2
   10  CONTINUE
       SCALR = VSCALR(N)
       RETURN
       END

       SUBROUTINE VSUB2 (N, SCA, VSCALR)
       DIMENSION SCA(*), VSCALR(*)
       COMMON /SCALAR/ SCALR
       DO 10 I = 1, N
         SCA(I) = SCA(I) + VSCALR(I)
   10  CONTINUE
       RETURN
       END
```

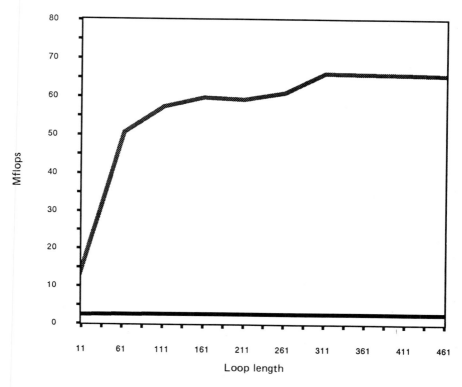

FIGURE 4.48
Performance Comparison of Loops 48080 and 48081, Cray
X-MP. Original, solid line; restructured, dotted line.

Our final example in loop 48090 combines the problem of a wrap-around scalar ET with a call to the routine SSSUB. The setting of ET is actually hidden from the compiler, since it is within SSSUB. Expanding the code in line exposes the problem, and we solve it by promoting ET to the array VET as shown in loop 48091. The performance improvement depicted in Figure 4.49 exceeds a factor of 15.

```
C       THE ORIGINAL
        ET = 0.0
        DO 48090 I = 1, N
         B(I) = SQRT (F(I)**2 + E(I)**2) + ET
         CALL SSSUB (B(I), ET, C(I), D(I), PI)
         A(I) = SQRT (ABS (D(I) ) )
48090 CONTINUE
        SUBROUTINE SSSUB (Y1, Y2, Y3, Y4, PI)
        Y4 = Y1**2 + Y3**2 * SQRT (ABS (Y1 + Y3) )
        Y2 = PI * Y3 + Y3
        Y4 = Y2 + Y4
        RETURN
        END
```

```
C       THE RESTRUCTURED
        VET(1)=0.0
        DO 48091 I = 1, N
        VET(I+1) = PI * C(I) + C(I)
        B(I) = SQRT (F(I)**2 + E(I)**2) + VET(I)
        D(I) = B(I)**2 + C(I)**2 * SQRT (ABS (B(I) + C(I) ) )
        D(I) = VET(I+1) + D(I)
        A(I) = SQRT (ABS (D(I) ) )
48091 CONTINUE
```

4.9.10   I/O Statements

The appearance of I/O statements in a loop must be treated as the appearance of a subprogram reference. That is, an I/O statement will prevent optimization of the rest of the code in a loop. It may be split out into a separate loop if it is not referencing variables and arrays referenced elsewhere in the loop (including other subprograms called from within the loop).

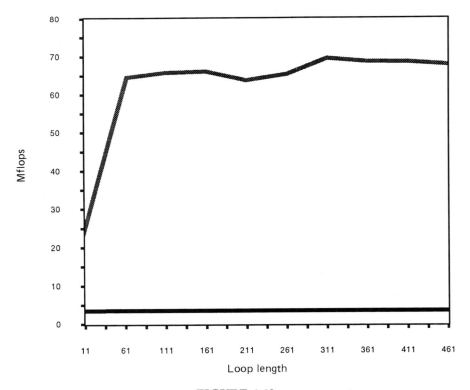

FIGURE 4.49

Performance Comparison of Loops 48090 and 48091, Cray X-MP. Original, solid line; restructured, dotted line.

4.9.11   Assigned GO TO Statements

An assigned GO TO contains hidden information that cannot be known at compile time, and therefore the associated code cannot be optimized. In general, and unlike a computed GO TO, it is impossible to know to which labels an assigned GO TO can jump. To optimize a loop such as 48100 requires a rewrite of the subprogram to eliminate the use of assigned GO TOs.

```
      ASSIGN 10 TO LABEL
         . . .
      IF (condition) ASSIGN 100 TO LABEL
         . . .
      DO 48100 I = 1, N
         . . .
      GO TO LABEL
         . . .
48100 CONTINUE
```

4.9.12   Backward GO TOs

Backward GO TOs in a DO loop can frequently be rewritten as forward transfers. An exception occurs when the backward transfer is being used to loop on convergence to a desired value. If this occurs, the code can be rewritten as a DO loop with a jump out of the loop when convergence is obtained. Then techniques discussed in Section 4.9.8 can be used to restructure the new loop.

4.10
SUMMARY

This chapter has covered a large number of techniques that can be used to optimize Fortran programs for supercomputers. Some of the techniques will even help scalar computers to run faster. The "real world" contains application codes much more complex then these examples. But these complicated codes can usually be optimized with a judicious application of a sequence of these techniques. At times, loops may be pulled into a routine, switched with shorter inner loops, and IF statements simplified so that a compiler can effectively optimize the code.

Problems

1. How would you expect the following two loops to compare in execution time for large N?

```
          DO 10 I = 1, N
          A(I) = EXP (B(I))
10        CONTINUE

          DO 20    I=1, N
          A(IA(I)) = EXP (B(IB(I))
20        CONTINUE
```

2. How would you restructure the following loop for optimal vector performance?

```
          DO 101   J = 2 ,N
          AH = B(J) - B(J-1)
          DO 100   I = 2, N
          A(I,J) = AH * A(I-1,J) + C(I,J)
100       CONTINUE
          BH = D(J) - D(J-1)
          DO 102   I = N, 2, -1
          A(I,J) = BH * A(I+1,J) + C(I,J)
102       CONTINUE
101       CONTINUE
```

3. Compute average vector length for diagonals in an M × N rectangular grid. Derive the equation for the average number of points on a planar slice through an N-dimensional grid.

4. In restructuring the loops in Section 4.9.4, some have an order-of-magnitude performance improvement, and others improve by as little as 20–50%. Match up the reasons for the improvement (second column) obtained for the following original loops (first column):

   1. 43020 a. Original vectorized and the restructured is a little more efficient.

   2. 43030 b. Large amount of overhead that the original does not have.

   3. 43070 c. Vectorize only a portion of the total calculations in the loop.

   4. 43080 d. Restructuring obtains good increase (factor 7–10).

   5. 43090 e. Additional memory required. (Although this does not effect performance, it is important to realize.)

   6. 43100

   7. 43140

Note: Some may have multiple answers.

5. If a compiler will not vectorize loop 44022, how would you restructure to obtain vectorization?

6. Most machines have optimized library packages that include the "Basic Linear Algebra Subroutines" (BLAS).* Which BLAS routine could be used to replace loop 44042?

7. In the restructuring of loops 44055 and 44060, notice that the difference in timings grows smaller for longer number of iterations. In fact, in loop 44060, they even cross. What does this tell you about the dot-product routine?

8. In loop nest 45011 we see that the outer loop is the preferred loop for vectorization, even if it has the same number of loop iterations as the inner loop. Several reasons exist for such a situation. Can you name three?

9. Suppose that in loops 46011 and 46020, the short-loop iteration count is specified by a variable (e.g., NN), rather than the literal constant 4. Suppose further that you know that NN is always in the range 1 to 8. How would you write an optimized version of these loops? (Hint: The restructuring may generate more lines of code; but it will run much quicker.)

10. In the restructuring for loop 42020, how many temporary arrays are needed for the restructuring? How might we organize temporary array usage to minimize the overall amount of storage required by the job?

11. In loop 47133 why do we use a maximum length of 128 rather than 64? Would 256 be better?

12. By using a simple operation count, what percentage of the calculations are vectorized in the restructuring of loop 48010? (Count the divide operation as 4.) What improvement would you expect from the amount of vectorization? What other factors may reduce the overall improvement?

13. Which of the restructured loops in Chapter 4 would execute faster than the original on a scalar machine?

14. On a Cray system, use the MXM routine for matrix multiply and compare the timing to the Fortran version of loop 46032.

* C. Lawson, R. Hanson, D. Kincaid, and F. Krogh, "Basic Linear Algebra Subprograms for Fortran Usage," ACM Transactions on Mathematical Software 5 (1979), pp. 308–323.

Appendix A
ABBREVIATIONS AND GLOSSARY

A.1 Common Abbreviations

ALU: arithmetic and logical unit
ANSI: American National Standards Institute
CDC: Control Data Corporation
CII: constant increment integer
CIV: constant increment variable
CPU: central processing unit
CRI: Cray Research Incorporated
FOLR: first order linear recurrence
IBM: International Business Machines
IPS: instructions per second
Mflops: millions of floating-point operations per second
MIMD: multiple instruction stream, multiple data stream
MISD: multiple instruction stream, single data stream
MIPS: millions of instructions per second
NEC: Nippon Electric Corporation
SIMD: single instruction stream, multiple data stream
SISD: single instruction stream, single data stream

A.2 Glossary of Terms

array constant Within a DO loop, an array reference all of whose subscripts are invariant.

```
      DO 10 I = 1, N
        A(I) = X(J) * B(I) + Z(8,J,K,3)
   10 CONTINUE
```

In the preceding loop, X(J) and Z(8,J,K,3) are array constants.

bank cycle time The time, measured in clock cycles, taken by a memory bank between the honoring of one request to fetch or store a data item and accepting another such request. On most supercomputers this value is either four or eight clock cycles.

cache   A small, fast memory placed between the main memory of a computer and its very fast CPU registers. It is intended to keep moderately large blocks of often-used data close to the CPU.

chime   "Chained vector time." Approximately equal to the vector length in a DO loop. The number of chimes required for a loop dominates the time required for execution. A new chime begins in a loop each time a resource (functional unit, vector register, or memory path) must be reused.

clock cycle   The time duration of the square wave pulse sent throughout a computer to synchronize operations. For example, the clock cycle of a Cray-2 is 4.1 nsec.

common subexpression   A combination of operations and operands that is repeated, especially in a loop

```
      DO 20 I = 1, N
        A(I) = 2.0 + B(I) * C(I) + X(I) / T(I)
        Y(I) = P(I) / (2.0 + B(I) * C(I))
        D(I) = X(I) / T(I) + U(I)
   20 CONTINUE
```

The following are common subexpressions in the preceding loop:

```
    2.0 + B(I) * C(I)

    X(I)/T(I)
```

A good compiler will not recompute the common subexpressions but will save them in a register for reuse.

compiler directives   Special keywords specified on a comment card, but recognizable by a particular compiler as providing additional user information for use in optimization. For example,

```
    CDIR$ IVDEP
```

specifies to a Cray compiler that no recursive relationships occur among the array references in the loop following the directive.

concurrent processing   Simultaneous execution of instructions by two or more processors within a computer.

data dependency   A relationship between Fortran statements such that one of the statements depends on the results of the other. For example:

```
    S1 = A + B

    S2 = S1 * X + Y
```

The second statement is *data dependent* on the first—that is, they must be executed in the order shown. A recursive data dependency involves statements in a DO loop such that a statement in one iteration depends on the results of a statement from a previous iteration. For example:

```
DO 30 I = 1, N
   A(I) = B(I) * A(I-1) + C(I)
30 CONTINUE
```

The assignment statement in loop 30 is self-referent; that is, the value A(I) computed in one iteration is the value A(I−1) needed in the next.

functional units   Functionally independent parts of the ALU of a computer, such that many operations may proceed in parallel; for example, address calculation, floating-point add, floating-point multiply, and so forth.

instruction scheduling   A strategy of a compiler. The intent is to analyze the outcome of the operations specified in a program and to issue instructions in an optimal manner. That is, the instructions are not necessarily issued in the order specified by the programmer, but in an order that optimally uses the registers, functional units, and memory paths of the computer—at the same time guaranteeing correct results for the computation.

instruction set   The capabilities of a particular computer, as specified in a machine code (and often in assembler mnemonics).

invariant   A variable, especially in a DO loop, that appears only on the right side of equals signs. That is, it is never assigned a new value.

invariant expression   An expression all of whose operands are invariants or constants.

memory-bank conflict   A condition that occurs when a memory unit receives a request to fetch or store a data item prior to completion of its bank cycle time since its last such request.

minisupercomputer   A computer designed to have many of the architectural features of a supercomputer, but having a clock cycle and price more comparable to a minicomputer.

multiple instruction stream, multiple data stream (MIMD)   A computer design that involves two or more functionally independent processors capable of operating on different data streams in parallel.

multiple instruction stream, single data stream (MISD)   A name for a computer design that has perhaps never been realized, but implies that two or more processors would operate on a single stream of data.

nanosecond (nsec)   A billionth of a second: 1.0×10^{-9} seconds.

optimization   A process whereby a compiler tries to make optimal use of the target computer's hardware to perform the operations specified by a programmer. Or, the process whereby a programmer tries to make optimal use of his or her target language to cause the compiler to produce optimal code.

optimization block   A block of code (rarely a whole subprogram, often a single DO loop) in which a compiler optimizes the generated code. A few compilers attempt to optimize across such blocks; many work on each block independently.

parallel processing   The simultaneous processing of instructions by two or more processors within a single computer. SIMD and MIMD are two different kinds of parallel processing.

parsing   The process whereby a compiler analyzes the syntax of a program to establish the relationships among operators, operands, and other tokens of a program. Parsing does not involve any semantic analysis.

physical memory   The actual memory of a computer directly available for fetching or storing of data (contrast with *virtual memory*).

pipeline   A term denoting a mechanism inside all supercomputers that allows new operands to begin processing in each clock cycle and moves partially completed operations along an assembly line inside the CPU, generally producing one result per clock cycle at the end of each pipeline.

pseudovector   A scalar temporary.

recursion   See *data dependency* (recursive).

reduction function   An algorithm that receives a vector of values as input and generates a single scalar value result. The variable containing the result is referred to as a "reduction-function scalar." As typically coded in Fortran, most compilers recognize such reduction functions as sum (product) of the elements of a vectorizable expression, for example, dot product, the minimum (maximum) of the elements of a vectorizable expression, and several variants on these themes.

scalar processing   The processing of a code using instructions that can operate on a single pair of operands at a time (contrast with *vector processing*).

scalar temporary   A scalar variable set equal to a vectorizable expression on each iteration of a DO loop.

single instruction stream, multiple data stream (SIMD) A computer design that provides for processing of instructions from a single stream, but providing simultaneous computation of results from multiple data streams. Two principal designs are often described as SIMD: 1) a single CPU with its ALU realized as a set of functional units; and 2) a separate instruction processor sending identical instruction streams to two or more ALUs.

single instruction stream, single data stream (SISD) A conventional, typically inexpensive computer. Each instruction from a single instruction stream is performed to completion before the next instruction is begun.

strength reduction A process whereby a compiler attempts to replace instructions specified by the programmer with less costly instructions that produce identical results, for example, X**2 becomes X*X.

stripmining A process used by a compiler on a register-to-register vector processor whereby a DO loop of long or variable iteration count is performed in "strips" of operands. The length of each strip is equal to the length of a vector register, except for a "remainder" strip whose length is generally less. So, for example, on a Cray computer, a loop of iteration count 150 is performed in one strip of length 22 (the remainder) then two strips of length 64. This technique can also be used by a programmer to vectorize a loop of indeterminate length, that is, a loop containing a GO TO that jumps out of the loop.

supercomputer A casual term describing members of a class of the larger, faster scientific computers, usually having vector or parallel architecture.

superword A term used on the CYBER 205 and the ETA 10 to describe a conglomerate of eight 64 bit words, or, alternately, sixteen 32-bit "half-words." The memory units on these machines generally fetch and store data in superwords (also called "swords"), regardless of the size of the data item referenced by the user program.

thrashing A phenomenon of virtual memory systems that occurs when the program itself, by the manner in which it is referencing its data and instructions, regularly causes the next memory locations to be referenced to have been overwritten by recent or current instructions. The result is that referenced items are rarely in the machine's physical memory and almost always must be fetched from secondary storage, usually a disk. When this occurs, the elapsed time of the program generally follows the disk speed rather than the speed of electronic memory.

unneeded store When two or more stores into the same memory location occur within an optimization block, especially within a DO loop, only the last store need actually be performed; the rest are unneeded, and will not be performed by the compiler. A programmer may take advantage of this by assigning temporary results to an array that is also set later in a loop, as in loop 40:

```
      DO 40 I = 1, N
      A(I) = B(I) * C(I) / (E(I) + F(I))
      X(I) = Y(I) * A(I)
      Z(I) = R(I) + Q(I) * A(I)
      A(I) = X(I) + Y(I) * Z(I)
   40 CONTINUE
```

vector   An ordered list of items in a computer's memory, contained within a Fortran array. A simple vector is defined as having a starting address, a length, and a stride. An indirect address vector is defined as having a relative base address and a vector of values to be applied as indexes to the base. Consider:

```
      DO 50 I = 1, N
      J = J * J / I
      K = K + 2
      A(I) = B(IB(I)) * C(K) + D(J)
   50 CONTINUE
```

All of the vectors above have length N; A and C are simple vectors with strides of one and two, respectively; B is an indirect address vector with the simple vector IB holding the indexes; and the vector of indirect address indexes of D can be computed at execution time from the initial value of J.

vector processing   The processing of a code using instructions that operate on all of the elements of an ordered list of operands, usually in a pipelined manner (contrast with *scalar processing*).

vectorize   The process whereby a compiler generates vector instructions for a loop. Also the process whereby a programmer restructures a program to cause the compiler to vectorize the important loops.

virtual memory   An address-mapping scheme that provides a programmer with a significantly larger memory than that physically available on a given computer. As data items are referenced within a program, the system assigns them to actual physical memory locations. Infrequently referenced items are transparently migrated to and from secondary storage — often, disks. The collection of physical memory locations assigned to a program is its "working set."

von Neumann machine   A scalar processor in which one instruction at a time is decoded and performed to completion before the next instruction is decoded. A SISD machine.

working set   See *virtual memory.*

wrap-around scalar   A scalar variable whose value set in one iteration of a DO loop is referenced in a subsequent iteration and is consequently recursive; easily recognized within most loops, because it is referenced before it is set. All common reduction-function scalars are wrap-around scalars and usually do not prevent vectorization. All other wrap-around scalars usually do prevent vectorization of the loop in which they appear. All scalars in the following loop are wrap around except S.

```
      DO 60 I = 1, N
        S = T
        T = A(I) * B(I)
        SUM = SUM + T/S
        IF (T.GT.0) THEN
          Q = X(I) + Y(I) / Z(I)
        ENDIF
        R(I) = Q + P(I)
   60 CONTINUE
```

The scalar Q is wrap around because on any iteration for which (T.GT.0) is not true, the value used to compute R(I) wraps around from the previous iteration.

Appendix B
EXAMPLES OF THE FORGE TIMING FACILITY

B.1 Timing Results from LINPACK Benchmark

TIMING SUMMARY BY SUBPROGRAM

SUBPROGRAM	INCL. TIME	EXCL. TIME	CALLS	AVG/CALL	INCL%	EXCL%
1 SLINP	2.210606880	0.003177797	1	0.0003177797	100.0	0.1
2 MATGEN	0.555042013	0.555042013	27	0.020557112	25.1	25.1
3 SGEFA	1.592775178	0.855313813	26	0.032896685	72.1	38.7
4 ISAMAX	0.066317154	0.066317154	2574	0.000025764	3.0	3.0
5 SSCAL	0.013856947	0.013856947	2574	0.000005383	0.6	0.6
6 SAXPY	0.683476285	0.683476285	133874	0.000005105	30.9	30.9
7 SGESL	0.059471378	0.033282357	26	0.001280091	2.7	1.5
8 SMXPY	0.000138624	0.000138624	1	0.000138624	0.0	0.0
9 EFSLON	0.000001891	0.000001891	1	0.000001891	0.0	0.0
TOTALS =>	2.210606880	2.210606880	139104			100.0

Average time per call is computed from the exclusive execution times.
The percentages are over the total execution time for that portion of
the program clocked by FORGE.

188

```
>=
```

CALLED FROM	CALLS	AVG TIME/CALL	INCL. TIME	% JOB XEQ TIME IN ROUTINE SLINP
PROGRAM	1	2.210607	2.210607	100.0 WHEN CALLED FROM *PROGRAM*
TOTAL ->	1	2.210607	2.210607	100.0 % TOTAL JOB XEQ TIME SPENT IN ROUTINE SLINP

> NESTING	PROCEDURE OR DO-LOOP IDENTIFIER	INCLUSIVE %JOB:%ROUTINE	EXCLUSIVE %JOB:%ROUTINE	COUNT	DO-LOOP-LENGTH AVERAGE	MAXIMUM
	SLINP	100.0:100.0	0.1: 0.1	1		
1	MATGEN	6.5: 6.5	6.5: 6.5	7		
1	SGEFA	16.6: 16.6	9.0: 9.0	6		
1	SGESL	0.6: 0.6	0.4: 0.4	6		
1	DO 10 i =1,n	0.0: 0.0	0.0: 0.0	1	100	100
1	DO 20 i =1,n	0.0: 0.0	0.0: 0.0	1	100	100
1	SMXPY	0.0: 0.0	0.0: 0.0	1		
1	DO 30 i =1,n	0.0: 0.0	0.0: 0.0	1	100	100
1	EPSLON	0.0: 0.0	0.0: 0.0	1		
1	DO 90 i =1,ntimes	37.0: 37.0	0.0: 0.0	1	10	10
2	MATGEN	9.3: 9.3	9.3: 9.3	10		
2	SGEFA	27.7: 27.7	15.0: 15.0	10		
1	DO 100 i =1,ntimes	1.0: 1.0	0.0: 0.0	1	10	10
2	SGESL	1.0: 1.0	0.6: 0.6	10		
1	DO 120 i =1,ntimes	37.0: 37.0	0.0: 0.0	1	10	10
2	MATGEN	9.3: 9.3	9.3: 9.3	10		
2	SGEFA	27.7: 27.7	14.7: 14.7	10		
1	DO 130 i =1,ntimes	1.0: 1.0	0.0: 0.0	1	10	10
2	SGESL	1.0: 1.0	0.6: 0.6	10		

>=

MATGEN

CALLED FROM	CALLS	AVG TIME/CALL	INCL. TIME	% JOB XEQ TIME IN ROUTINE MATGEN
SLINP	27	0.020557	0.555042	25.1 WHEN CALLED FROM SLINP
TOTAL ->	27	0.020557	0.555042	25.1 % TOTAL JOB XEQ TIME SPENT IN ROUTINE MATGEN

> NESTING	PROCEDURE OR DO-LOOP IDENTIFIER	INCLUSIVE %JOB:%ROUTNE	EXCLUSIVE %JOB:%ROUTNE	COUNT	DO-LOOP-LENGTH AVERAGE	MAXIMUM
	MATGEN	25.1:100.0	0.0: 0.0	27		
1	DO 30 j =1,n	24.8: 99.0	0.2: 0.9	27	100	100
2	DO 20 i =1,n	24.6: 98.1	24.6: 98.1	2700	100	100
1	DO 35 i =1,n	0.0: 0.0	0.0: 0.0	27	100	100
1	DO 50 j =1,n	0.2: 1.0	0.2: 0.9	27	100	100
2	DO 40 i =1,n	0.0: 0.1	0.0: 0.1	2700	100	100

>=

SGEFA

CALLED FROM	CALLS	AVG TIME/CALL	INCL. TIME	% JOB XEQ TIME IN ROUTINE SGEFA
SLINP	26	0.061261	1.592775	72.1 WHEN CALLED FROM SLINP
TOTAL ->	26	0.061261	1.592775	72.1 % TOTAL JOB XEQ TIME SPENT IN ROUTINE SGEFA

> NESTING	PROCEDURE OR DO-LOOP IDENTIFIER	INCLUSIVE %JOB:%ROUTNE	EXCLUSIVE %JOB:%ROUTNE	COUNT	DO-LOOP-LENGTH AVERAGE	MAXIMUM
	SGEFA	72.1:100.0	0.0: 0.0	26		
1	DO 60 k =1,nm1	72.0:100.0	1.2: 1.7	26	99	99
2	ISAMAX	3.0: 4.2	3.0: 4.2	2574		
2	SSCAL	0.6: 0.9	0.6: 0.9	2574		
2	DO 30 j =kp1,n	67.2: 93.3	37.5: 52.0	2574	50	99
3	SAXPY	29.7: 41.3	29.7: 41.3	128700		

ISAMAX

CALLED FROM	CALLS	AVG TIME/CALL	INCL. TIME	% JOB XEQ TIME IN ROUTINE ISAMAX
SGEFA	2574	0.000026	0.066317	3.0 WHEN CALLED FROM SGEFA
TOTAL ->	2574	0.000026	0.066317	3.0 % TOTAL JOB XEQ TIME SPENT IN ROUTINE ISAMAX

> NESTING	PROCEDURE OR DO-LOOP IDENTIFIER	INCLUSIVE %JOB:%ROUTINE	EXCLUSIVE %JOB:%ROUTINE	COUNT	DO-LOOP-LENGTH AVERAGE	MAXIMUM
	ISAMAX	3.0:100.0	0.4: 14.6	2574		
1	DO 30 i =2,n	2.6: 85.4	2.6: 85.4	2574	50	99

SSCAL

CALLED FROM	CALLS	AVG TIME/CALL	INCL. TIME	% JOB XEQ TIME IN ROUTINE SSCAL
SGEFA	2574	0.000005	0.013857	0.6 WHEN CALLED FROM SGEFA
TOTAL ->	2574	0.000005	0.013857	0.6 % TOTAL JOB XEQ TIME SPENT IN ROUTINE SSCAL

> NESTING	PROCEDURE OR DO-LOOP IDENTIFIER	INCLUSIVE %JOB:%ROUTINE	EXCLUSIVE %JOB:%ROUTINE	COUNT	DO-LOOP-LENGTH AVERAGE	MAXIMUM
	SSCAL	0.6:100.0	0.4: 60.6	2574		
1	DO 30 i =1,m	0.1: 23.4	0.1: 23.4	2080	2	4
1	DO 50 i =mp1,n,5	0.1: 16.0	0.1: 16.0	2470	10	19

SAXPY

CALLED FROM	CALLS	AVG TIME/CALL	INCL. TIME	% JOB XEQ TIME IN ROUTINE SAXPY
SGEFA	128700	0.000005	0.657287	29.7 WHEN CALLED FROM SGEFA
SGESL	5174	0.000005	0.026189	1.2 WHEN CALLED FROM SGESL
TOTAL ->	133874	0.000005	0.683476	30.9 % TOTAL JOB XEQ TIME SPENT IN ROUTINE SAXPY

> NESTING	PROCEDURE OR DO-LOOP IDENTIFIER	INCLUSIVE %JOB:%ROUTINE	EXCLUSIVE %JOB:%ROUTINE	COUNT	DO-LOOP-LENGTH AVERAGE	MAXIMUM
	SAXPY	30.9:100.0	22.6: 73.1	133874		
1	DO 30 i =1,m	6.2: 20.0	6.2: 20.0	101400	2	3
1	DO 50 i =mp1,n,4	2.1: 6.9	2.1: 6.9	133536	16	24

SGESL

CALLED FROM	CALLS	AVG TIME/CALL	INCL. TIME	% JOB XEQ TIME IN ROUTINE SGESL
SLINP	26	0.002287	0.059471	2.7 WHEN CALLED FROM SLINP
TOTAL ->	26.	0.002287	0.059471	2.7 % TOTAL JOB XEQ TIME SPENT IN ROUTINE SGESL

> NESTING	PROCEDURE OR DO-LOOP IDENTIFIER	INCLUSIVE %JOB:%ROUTINE	EXCLUSIVE %JOB:%ROUTINE	COUNT	DO-LOOP-LENGTH AVERAGE	MAXIMUM
	SGESL	2.7:100.0	0.0: 0.3	26		
1	DO 20 k =1,nm1	1.3: 50.1	0.8: 28.1	26	99	99
2	SAXPY	0.6: 22.0	0.6: 22.0	2574		
1	DO 40 kb =1,n	1.3: 49.6	0.7: 27.5	26	100	100
2	SAXPY	0.6: 22.1	0.6: 22.1	2600		

192

>=

SMXPY

CALLED FROM	CALLS	AVG TIME/CALL	INCL. TIME	% JOB XEQ TIME IN ROUTINE SMXPY
SLINP	1	0.000139	0.000139	0.0 WHEN CALLED FROM SLINP
TOTAL ->	1	0.000139	0.000139	0.0 % TOTAL JOB XEQ TIME SPENT IN ROUTINE SMXPY

> NESTING	PROCEDURE OR DO-LOOP IDENTIFIER	INCLUSIVE %JOB:%ROUTNE	EXCLUSIVE %JOB:%ROUTNE	COUNT	DO-LOOP-LENGTH AVERAGE	MAXIMUM
	SMXPY	0.0:100.0	0.0: 3.4	1		
1	DO 30 i =1,n1	0.0: 3.7	0.0: 3.7	1	100	100
1	DO 60 j =jmin,n2,16	0.0: 92.9	0.0: 9.7	1	6	6
2	DO 50 i =1,n1	0.0: 83.2	0.0: 83.2	6	100	100

>=

EPSLON

CALLED FROM	CALLS	AVG TIME/CALL	INCL. TIME	% JOB XEQ TIME IN ROUTINE EPSLON
SLINP	1	0.000002	0.000002	0.0 WHEN CALLED FROM SLINP
TOTAL ->	1	0.000002	0.000002	0.0 % TOTAL JOB XEQ TIME SPENT IN ROUTINE EPSLON

> NESTING	PROCEDURE OR DO-LOOP IDENTIFIER	INCLUSIVE %JOB:%ROUTNE	EXCLUSIVE %JOB:%ROUTNE	COUNT	DO-LOOP-LENGTH AVERAGE	MAXIMUM
	EPSLON	0.0:100.0	0.0:100.0	1		

CALL CHAIN MAP

Each DO loop and subprogram call made in the timed portion of the program is listed below with the nesting level indicated by indenting. The counts give the number of times a subprogram or loop was entered. [nn] shows the average length of a DO loop. The percentages show the inclusive and exclusive time for that DO loop or subprogram call over that portion of job execution timed.

NESTING	COUNT	INCL%	EXCL%	CALL CHAIN
0	1	100.0	0.1	SLINP
1	7	6.5	0.0	-MATGEN
2	7	6.4	0.1	--MATGEN/DO 30 j =1,n [100]
3	700	6.4	6.4	---MATGEN/DO 20 i =1,n [100]
2	7	0.0	0.0	--MATGEN/DO 35 i =1,n [100]
2	7	0.1	0.1	--MATGEN/DO 50 j =1,n [100]
3	700	0.0	0.0	---MATGEN/DO 40 i =1,n [100]
1	6	16.6	0.0	-SGEFA
2	6	16.6	0.3	--SGEFA/DO 60 k =1,nm1 [99]
3	594	0.7	0.1	---ISAMAX
4	594	0.6	0.6	----ISAMAX/DO 30 i =2,n [50]
3	594	0.1	0.1	---SSCAL
4	480	0.0	0.0	----SSCAL/DO 30 i =1,m [2]
4	570	0.0	0.0	----SSCAL/DO 50 i =mp1,n,5 [10]
3	594	15.5	8.7	---SGEFA/DO 30 j =kp1,n [50]
4	29700	6.8	5.0	----SAXPY
5	22500	1.4	1.4	-----SAXPY/DO 30 i =1,m [2]
5	29664	0.5	0.5	-----SAXPY/DO 50 i =mp1,n,4 [16]
1	6	0.6	0.0	-SGESL
2	6	0.3	0.2	--SGESL/DO 20 k =1,nm1 [99]
3	594	0.1	0.1	---SAXPY
4	450	0.0	0.0	----SAXPY/DO 30 i =1,m [2]
4	576	0.0	0.0	----SAXPY/DO 50 i =mp1,n,4 [12]
2	6	0.3	0.2	--SGESL/DO 40 kb =1,n [100]
3	600	0.1	0.1	---SAXPY
4	450	0.0	0.0	----SAXPY/DO 30 i =1,m [2]
4	576	0.0	0.0	----SAXPY/DO 50 i =mp1,n,4 [12]
1	1	0.0	0.0	-SLINP/DO 10 i =1,n [100]
1	1	0.0	0.0	-SLINP/DO 20 i =1,n [100]
1	1	0.0	0.0	-SMXPY
2	1	0.0	0.0	--SMXPY/DO 30 i =1,n1 [100]
2	1	0.0	0.0	--SMXPY/DO 60 j =jmin,n2,16 [6]
3	6	0.0	0.0	---SMXPY/DO 50 i =1,n1 [100]
1	1	0.0	0.0	-SLINP/DO 30 i =1,n [100]

Profiling listing (call-tree with call counts and percent-of-time columns). Left column read first, then right column.

```
1     1     0.0   0.0  -EPSLON
1     1    37.0   0.0  -SLINF/DO 90 i =1,ntimes [10]
2    10     9.3   0.1  --MATGEN
3    10     9.2   9.1  ---MATGEN/DO 30 j =1,n [100]
4  1000     9.1   0.0  ----MATGEN/DO 20 i =1,n [100]
3    10     0.0   0.1  ---MATGEN/DO 35 i =1,n [100]
3    10     0.1   0.0  ---MATGEN/DO 50 j =1,n [100]
4  1000     0.0   0.0  ----MATGEN/DO 40 i =1,n [100]
2    10    27.7   0.0  --SGEFA
3    10    27.7   0.5  ---SGEFA/DO 60 k =1,nm1 [99]
4   990     1.2   0.2  ----ISAMAX
5   990     1.0   1.0  -----ISAMAX/DO 30 i =2,n [50]
4   990     0.2   0.1  ----SSCAL
5   800     0.1   0.1  -----SSCAL/DO 30 i =1,m [2]
5   950     0.0   0.0  -----SSCAL/DO 50 j =mp1,n,5 [10]
4   990    25.8  14.5  ----SGEFA/DO 30 j =kp1,n [50]
5   990    11.3   8.3  -----SAXPY
6 37500     2.2   2.2  ------SAXPY/DO 30 i =1,m [2]
6 49440     0.8   0.8  ------SAXPY/DO 50 i =mp1,n,4 [16]
1     1     1.0   0.0  -SLINF/DO 100 i =1,ntimes [10]
2    10     1.0   0.0  --SGESL
3    10     0.5   0.3  ---SGESL/DO 20 k =1,nm1 [99]
4   990     0.2   0.2  ----SAXPY
5   750     0.0   0.0  -----SAXPY/DO 30 i =1,m [2]
5   960     0.0   0.0  -----SAXPY/DO 50 i =mp1,n,4 [12]
3    10     0.5   0.3  ---SGESL/DO 40 kb =1,n [100]
4   990     0.2   0.2  ----SAXPY
5   750     0.0   0.0  -----SAXPY/DO 30 i =1,m [2]
5   960     0.0   0.0  -----SAXPY/DO 50 i =mp1,n,4 [12]
1     1    37.0   0.0  -SLINF/DO 120 i =1,ntimes [10]
2    10     9.3   0.1  --MATGEN
3    10     9.2   9.1  ---MATGEN/DO 30 j =1,n [100]
4  1000     9.1   0.0  ----MATGEN/DO 20 i =1,n [100]
3    10     0.0   0.1  ---MATGEN/DO 35 i =1,n [100]
3    10     0.1   0.0  ---MATGEN/DO 50 j =1,n [100]
4  1000     0.0   0.0  ----MATGEN/DO 40 i =1,n [100]
2    10    27.7   0.0  --SGEFA
3    10    27.7   0.5  ---SGEFA/DO 60 k =1,nm1 [99]
4   990     1.2   0.2  ----ISAMAX
5   990     1.0   1.0  -----ISAMAX/DO 30 i =2,n [50]
4   990     0.2   0.1  ----SSCAL
5   800     0.1   0.1  -----SSCAL/DO 30 i =1,m [2]
5   950     0.0   0.0  -----SSCAL/DO 50 j =mp1,n,5 [10]
4   990    25.9  14.3  ----SGEFA/DO 30 j =kp1,n [50]
```

```
5 49500    11.6   8.4  -----SAXPY
6 37500     2.3   2.3  ------SAXPY/DO 30 i =1,m [2]
6 49440     0.8   0.8  ------SAXPY/DO 50 i =mp1,n,4 [16]
1     1     1.0   0.0  -SLINF/DO 130 i =1,ntimes [10]
2    10     1.0   0.0  --SGESL
3    10     0.5   0.3  ---SGESL/DO 20 k =1,nm1 [99]
4   990     0.2   0.2  ----SAXPY
5   750     0.0   0.0  -----SAXPY/DO 30 i =1,m [2]
5   960     0.0   0.0  -----SAXPY/DO 50 i =mp1,n,4 [12]
3    10     0.5   0.3  ---SGESL/DO 40 kb =1,n [100]
4   990     0.2   0.2  ----SAXPY
5   750     0.0   0.0  -----SAXPY/DO 30 i =1,m [2]
5   960     0.0   0.0  -----SAXPY/DO 50 i =mp1,n,4 [12]
```

B.2 Timing Results From HYGRIIID Program

P A C I F I C - S I E R R A   R E S E A R C H   F O R G E (TM)

DYNAMIC PROGRAM TIMING ANALYSIS USING PSR FORGE TIMING FACILITY >PSRTIM< VERSION 11 [Oct 87]

NOTE: Time spent in subprograms and DO-loops is tabulated below. Both INCLUSIVE and EXCLUSIVE times are given.
INCLUSIVE times include the time spent in a subprogram or loop and all the subprograms and loops entered from it.
The EXCLUSIVE time spent in a subprogram excludes the time spent in any subprograms entered from it. The
EXCLUSIVE time spent in a DO-loop excludes any loops or subprograms entered from it.

Results are only for that portion of the program instrumented by the FORGE clocking facility.
All timings are shown in seconds or percentages of job execution time.

TIMING SUMMARY BY SUBPROGRAM

	SUBPROGRAM	INCL. TIME	EXCL. TIME	CALLS	AVG/CALL	INCL%	EXCL%
1	HYGRIIID	4.944506376	0.003229824	1	0.003229824	100.0	0.1
2	INITIA	0.124968738	0.019750594	1	0.019750594	2.5	0.4
3	BODY	0.088449771	0.088449771	1	0.088449771	1.8	1.8
4	SAREA	0.015552587	0.002807282	2	0.001403641	0.3	0.1
5	METRIC	0.047880997	0.040050141	8	0.005006268	1.0	0.8
6	DYDX2	0.010994380	0.009967104	1380	0.000007223	0.2	0.2
7	Y2XANDZ	0.002147928	0.002147928	5700	0.000000377	0.0	0.0
8	DYDZ2	0.011678309	0.010620382	1380	0.000007696	0.2	0.2
9	EPSIL	0.000594877	0.000594877	1	0.000594877	0.0	0.0
10	CONVOL	0.002208719	0.002208719	4	0.000552180	0.0	0.0
11	OUTPT	0.094717306	0.094717306	4	0.023679327	1.9	1.9
12	STEP	4.721590508	0.297827956	3	0.099275985	95.5	6.0
13	RHS	1.588474840	0.334757809	3	0.111585936	32.1	6.8
14	CINVA	2.316640236	2.301798404	53100	0.000043348	46.9	46.6
15	AMATRX	0.060040445	0.060040445	21240	0.000002827	1.2	1.2
16	BMATRX	0.072406693	0.072406693	21240	0.000003409	1.5	1.5
17	BTRIP	0.843589821	0.816523495	177	0.004613127	17.1	16.5
18	LUDEC	0.053473791	0.053473791	21420	0.000002496	1.1	1.1
19	FILTRX	0.820671412	0.238488091	180	0.001324934	16.6	4.8
20	BTRI	0.372695695	0.346288230	180	0.001923824	7.5	7.0
21	ANGLES	0.148357532	0.148357532	10620	0.000013970	3.0	3.0
	TOTALS =>	4.944506376	4.944506376	136645			100.0

Average time per call is computed from the exclusive execution times.
The percentages are over the total execution time for that portion of
the program clocked by FORGE.

>=

CALLED FROM	CALLS	AVG TIME/CALL	INCL. TIME	% JOB XEQ TIME IN ROUTINE STEP
HYGRIIID	3	1.573864	4.721591	95.5 WHEN CALLED FROM HYGRIIID
TOTAL ->	3	1.573864	4.721591	95.5 % TOTAL JOB XEQ TIME SPENT IN ROUTINE STEP

> NESTING	PROCEDURE OR DO-LOOP IDENTIFIER	INCLUSIVE %JOB:%ROUTINE	EXCLUSIVE %JOB:%ROUTINE	COUNT	DO-LOOP-LENGTH AVERAGE	MAXIMUM
	STEP	95.5:100.0	0.0: 0.0	3		
1	DO 720 k =1,kmax	0.0: 0.4	0.0: 0.0	3	60	60
1	METRIC	0.3: 0.4	0.3: 0.3	3		
1	DO 94 k =1,kmax	0.0: 0.0	0.0: 0.0	3	60	60
1	DO 97 k =1,kmax	0.0: 0.0	0.0: 0.0	3	60	60
1	DO 45 it =1,itmax	95.1: 99.8	0.1: 0.2	3	1	1
2	METRIC	0.4: 0.4	0.3: 0.3	3		
2	RHS	32.1: 33.6	6.8: 7.1	3		
2	DO 20 j =jaend,jbend	33.2: 34.7	3.2: 3.4	3	59	59
3	BMATRX	0.7: 0.8	0.7: 0.8	10620		
3	CINVA	11.7: 12.2	11.6: 12.2	10620		
3	BTRIP	17.1: 17.9	16.5: 17.3	177		
3	DO 21 k =ka,kb	0.5: 0.5	0.2: 0.3	177	60	60
4	DO 22 n =1,3	0.2: 0.2	0.2: 0.2	10620	3	3
2	DO 30 k =ka,kb	29.3: 30.7	0.0: 0.0	3	60	60
3	FILTRX	16.6: 17.4	4.8: 5.1	180		
3	BTRI	7.5: 7.9	7.0: 7.3	180		
3	DO 36 j =1,jmax	5.1: 5.3	2.1: 2.2	180	60	60
4	ANGLES	3.0: 3.1	3.0: 3.1	10620		
2	DO 44 k =1,kmax	0.0: 0.0	0.0: 0.0	3	60	60
2	DO 45 k =1,kmax	0.0: 0.0	0.0: 0.0	3	60	60
3	Y2XANDZ	0.0: 0.0	0.0: 0.0	180		

CALLED FROM	CALLS	AVG TIME/CALL		RHS	INCL. TIME	% JOB XEQ TIME IN ROUTINE RHS
STEP	3	0.529492			1.588475	32.1 WHEN CALLED FROM STEP
TOTAL ->	3	0.529492			1.588475	32.1 % TOTAL JOB XEQ TIME SPENT IN ROUTINE RHS

> NESTING	PROCEDURE OR DO-LOOP IDENTIFIER	INCLUSIVE %JOB:%ROUTNE	EXCLUSIVE %JOB:%ROUTNE	COUNT	DO-LOOP-LENGTH AVERAGE	MAXIMUM
	RHS	32.1:100.0	0.0: 0.0	3		
1	CONVOL	0.0: 0.1	0.0: 0.1	3		
1	DO 10 j =ja,jb	2.7: 8.4	0.0: 0.0	3		
2	DO 10 k =ka,kb	2.7: 8.4	1.0: 3.0	174	58	58
3	CINVA	1.5: 4.5	1.5: 4.5	10440	60	60
3	DO 12 i =1,3	0.3: 0.8	0.3: 0.8	10440	3	3
1	DO 107 k =ka,kb	0.1: 0.4	0.0: 0.1	3	60	60
2	CINVA	0.1: 0.4	0.1: 0.2	180		
2	DO 112 i =1,3	0.0: 0.0	0.0: 0.0	180	3	3
1	DO 15 j =jaend,jbend	28.9: 90.0	0.0: 0.0	3	59	59
2	DO 15 k =ka,kb	28.9: 89.9	3.1: 9.7	177	60	60
3	AMATRX	0.6: 1.9	0.6: 1.9	10620		
3	BMATRX	0.7: 2.2	0.7: 2.2	10620		
3	CINVA	22.4: 69.8	22.3: 69.4	21240		
3	DO 16 n =1,3	1.6: 5.1	0.9: 2.8	10620	3	3
4	DO 16 m =1,3	0.7: 2.3	0.7: 2.3	31860	3	3
3	DO 18 n =1,3	0.4: 1.2	0.4: 1.2	10620	3	3
1	DO 20 j =jaend,jbend	0.2: 0.7	0.0: 0.0	3	59	59
2	DO 20 k =ka,kb	0.2: 0.7	0.2: 0.7	177	60	60
1	DO 30 k =ka,kb	0.1: 0.4	0.0: 0.0	3	60	60
2	DO 30 j =jaa,jbb	0.1: 0.4	0.1: 0.4	180	56	56
1	DO 31 k =ka,kb	0.0: 0.0	0.0: 0.0	3	60	60

```
>=
                                              CINVA

CALLED FROM    CALLS     AVG TIME/CALL    INCL. TIME    % JOB XEQ TIME IN ROUTINE CINVA

RHS            31860     0.000037         1.186398      24.0  WHEN CALLED FROM RHS
STEP           10620     0.000054         0.578007      11.7  WHEN CALLED FROM STEP
FILTRX         10620     0.000052         0.552236      11.2  WHEN CALLED FROM FILTRX

TOTAL ->       53100     0.000044         2.316640      46.9 % TOTAL JOB XEQ TIME SPENT IN ROUTINE CINVA
```

> NESTING PROCEDURE OR DO-LOOP IDENTIFIER	INCLUSIVE %JOB:%ROUTNE	EXCLUSIVE %JOB:%ROUTNE	COUNT	DO-LOOP-LENGTH AVERAGE	MAXIMUM
CINVA	46.9:100.0	8.9: 19.0	53100		
1 DYDX2	0.1: 0.1	0.1: 0.1	360		
1 DYDZ2	0.1: 0.1	0.1: 0.1	360		
1 DO 12 n =1,3	31.3: 66.8	3.7: 8.0	42480	3	3
2 DO 12 m =1,3	27.6: 58.9	17.0: 36.2	127440	3	3
3 DO 13 l =1,3	10.6: 22.6	10.6: 22.6	382320	3	3
1 DO 14 n =1,3	6.3: 13.5	4.6: 9.9	42480	3	3
2 DO 14 m =1,3	1.7: 3.6	1.7: 3.6	127440	3	3
1 DYDX2	0.1: 0.2	0.1: 0.2	540		
1 DYDZ2	0.1: 0.2	0.1: 0.2	540		

FILTRX

CALLED FROM	CALLS	AVG TIME/CALL	INCL. TIME	% JOB XEQ TIME IN ROUTINE FILTRX
STEP	180	0.004559	0.820871	16.6 WHEN CALLED FROM STEP
TOTAL ->	180	0.004559	0.820871	16.6 % TOTAL JOB XEQ TIME SPENT IN ROUTINE FILTRX

> NESTING	PROCEDURE OR DO-LOOP IDENTIFIER	INCLUSIVE %JOB:%ROUTNE	EXCLUSIVE %JOB:%ROUTNE	COUNT	DO-LOOP-LENGTH AVERAGE	MAXIMUM
	FILTRX	16.6:100.0	0.1: 0.3	180		
1	DO 10 j =ja,jb	16.2: 97.4	1.7: 10.0	180	58	58
2	AMATRX	0.6: 3.5	0.6: 3.5	10440		
2	CINVA	10.9: 65.7	10.9: 65.7	10440		
2	DO 12 n =1,3	3.0: 18.3	1.8: 10.9	10440	3	3
3	DO 13 m =1,3	1.2: 7.3	1.2: 7.3	31320	3	3
1	DO 40 n =1,3	0.0: 0.2	0.0: 0.1	180	3	3
2	DO 40 m =1,3	0.0: 0.1	0.0: 0.1	540	3	3
1	DO 41 n =1,3	0.0: 0.0	0.0: 0.0	180	3	3
1	AMATRX	0.0: 0.1	0.0: 0.0	180		
1	CINVA	0.3: 1.6	0.2: 1.3	180		
1	DO 172 n =1,3	0.0: 0.2	0.0: 0.1	180	3	3
2	DO 173 m =1,3	0.0: 0.1	0.0: 0.1	540	3	3

Appendix C
LOOPS FOR MEMORY-ACCESS COMPARISON

The following groups of loops are used to compare performance of three memory-access techniques in section 4.8: Group 1) indirect access with random indexing; Group 2) direct access with unitary stride; and Group 3) direct access with a stride of 128.

We are concerned here with the performance based on the ratio of operations to vector operands, and these ratios are listed in a comment preceding each loop. In other words, when the ratio is low, the loop spends more time accessing memory than in performing arithmetic, so the megaflop rating is correspondingly low. Conversely, those loops with many operations and just two vector operands achieve the highest performance numbers.

We expect that unitary stride will produce the best performance among the three groups. Indirect addressing adds one or more chimes to the computation because of the extra time needed to fetch the index, and causes general memory performance degradation due to both interference among the indexes and the requirement that the indexed array elements be delivered in the proper order. Finally, stride 128 forces memory-bank conflicts on each successive reference and slows the performance by a factor equal to the memory-bank cycle time. Performance comparisons for several machines are shown in section 4.8.

C.1 Group 1: Indirect Access with Random Index

```
C      ONE OPERATION - THREE OPERANDS      RATIO = 1/3
       DO 41000 I = 1, N
       A(IA(I)) = B(IA(I)) + C(IA(I))
41000 CONTINUE


C      ONE OPERATION - TWO OPERANDS      RATIO = 1/2
       DO 41001 I = 1, N
       A(IA(I)) = CO * B(IA(I))
41001 CONTINUE


C      TWO OPERATIONS - FOUR OPERANDS RATIO = 1/2
       DO 41002 I = 1, N
       A(IA(I)) = B(IA(I)) * C(IA(I)) + D(IA(I))
41002 CONTINUE
```

201

```
C     THREE OPERATIONS - FIVE OPERANDS     RATIO = 3/5
      DO 41003 I = 1, N
      A(IA(I)) = B(IA(I)) * C(IA(I)) + D(IA(I)) * E(IA(I))
41003 CONTINUE


C     TWO OPERATIONS - THREE OPERANDS     RATIO = 2/3
      DO 41004 I = 1, N
      A(IA(I)) = CO * B(IA(I)) + C(IA(I))
41004 CONTINUE


C     TWO OPERATIONS - TWO OPERANDS     RATIO = 1
      DO 41010 I = 1, N
      Y(IY(I)) = CO + X(IX(I)) * C1
41010 CONTINUE


C     THREE OPERATIONS - TWO OPERANDS     RATIO = 3/2
      DO 41011 I = 1, N
      Y(IY(I)) = CO + X(IX(I)) * (C1 + X(IX(I)) )
41011 CONTINUE


C     FIVE OPERATIONS - TWO OPERANDS     RATIO = 5/2
      DO 41012 I = 1, N
      Y(IY(I)) =  CO + X(IX(I)) * (C1 + X(IX(I))
     *           * (C2 + X(IX(I))                    ))
41012 CONTINUE


C     SEVEN OPERATIONS - TWO OPERANDS     RATIO = 7/2
      DO 41013 I = 1, N
      Y(IY(I)) =  CO + X(IX(I)) * (C1 + X(IX(I))
     *           * (C2 + X(IX(I)) * (C3 + X(IX(I)) )))
41013 CONTINUE


C     NINE OPERATIONS - TWO OPERANDS     RATIO = 9/2
      DO 41014 I = 1, N
      Y(IY(I)) =  CO + X(IX(I)) * (C1 + X(IX(I))
     *           * (C2 + X(IX(I)) * (C3 + X(IX(I))
     *           * (C4 + X(IX(I))                  ))))
41014 CONTINUE


C     ELEVEN OPERATIONS - TWO OPERANDS     RATIO = 11/2
      DO 41015 I = 1,N
      Y(IY(I)) =  CO + X(IX(I)) * (C1 + X(IX(I))
     *           * (C2 + X(IX(I)) * (C3 + X(IX(I))
     *           * (C4 + X(IX(I)) * (C5 + X(IX(I)) )))))
41015 CONTINUE


C     THIRTEEN OPERATIONS - TWO OPERANDS     RATIO = 13/2
      DO 41016 I = 1, N
      Y(IY(I)) =  CO + X(IX(I)) * (C1 + X(IX(I))
     *           * (C2 + X(IX(I)) * (C3 + X(IX(I))
     *           * (C4 + X(IX(I)) * (C5 + X(IX(I))
     *           * (C6 + X(IX(I))                  ))))))
41016 CONTINUE
```

```
C     FIFTEEN OPERATIONS - TWO OPERANDS     RATIO = 15/2
      DO 41017 I = 1, N
      Y(IY(I)) =  CO + X(IX(I)) * (C1 + X(IX(I))
     *            * (C2 + X(IX(I)) * (C3 + X(IX(I))
     *            * (C4 + X(IX(I)) * (C5 + X(IX(I))
     *            * (C6 + X(IX(I)) * (C7 + X(IX(I)) )))))))
41017 CONTINUE


C     SEVENTEEN OPERATIONS - TWO OPERANDS    RATIO = 17/2
      DO 41018 I = 1,N
      Y(IY(I)) =  CO + X(IX(I)) * (C1 + X(IX(I))
     *            * (C2 + X(IX(I)) * (C3 + X(IX(I))
     *            * (C4 + X(IX(I)) * (C5 + X(IX(I))
     *            * (C6 + X(IX(I)) * (C7 + X(IX(I))
     *            * (C8 + X(IX(I))                  ))))))))
41018 CONTINUE


C     NINETEEN OPERATIONS - TWO OPERANDS     RATIO = 19/2
      DO 41019 I = 1,N
      Y(IY(I)) =  CO + X(IX(I)) * (C1 + X(IX(I))
     *            * (C2 + X(IX(I)) * (C3 + X(IX(I))
     *            * (C4 + X(IX(I)) * (C5 + X(IX(I))
     *            * (C6 + X(IX(I)) * (C7 + X(IX(I))
     *            * (C8 + X(IX(I)) * (C9 + X(IX(I)) )))))))))
41019 CONTINUE
```

C.2   Group 2: Unitary Stride

```
C     ONE OPERATION - THREE OPERANDS     RATIO = 1/3
      DO 41020 I = 1, N
      A(I) = B(I) + C(I)
41020 CONTINUE


C     ONE OPERATION - TWO OPERANDS     RATIO = 1/2
      DO 41021 I = 1, N
      A(I) = CO * B(I)
41021 CONTINUE


C     TWO OPERATIONS - FOUR OPERANDS RATIO = 1/2
      DO 41022 I = 1,N
      A(I) = B(I)*C(I)+D(I)
41022 CONTINUE


C     THREE OPERATIONS - FIVE OPERANDS     RATIO = 3/5
      DO 41023 I=1, N
      A(I) = B(I) * C(I) + D(I) * E(I)
41023 CONTINUE


C     TWO OPERATIONS - THREE OPERANDS     RATIO = 2/3
      DO 41024 I=1, N
      A(I) = CO * B(I) + C(I)
41024 CONTINUE
```

```
C     TWO OPERATIONS - TWO OPERANDS      RATIO = 1
      DO 41030 I = 1, N
        Y(I) = CO + X(I) * C1
41030 CONTINUE


C     THREE OPERATIONS - TWO OPERANDS      RATIO = 3/2
      DO 41031 I = 1, N
        Y(I) = CO + X(I) * (C1 + X(I) )
41031 CONTINUE


C     FIVE OPERATIONS - TWO OPERANDS      RATIO = 5/2
      DO 41032 I = 1, N
        Y(I) = CO + X(I) * (C1 + X(I) * (C2 + X(I) ))
41032 CONTINUE


C     SEVEN OPERATIONS - TWO OPERANDS      RATIO = 7/2
      DO 41033 I = 1, N
        Y(I) = CO + X(I) * (C1 + X(I) * (C2 + X(I)
     *                  * (C3 + X(I)                )))
41033 CONTINUE


C     NINE OPERATIONS - TWO OPERANDS      RATIO = 9/2
      DO 41034 I = 1, N
        Y(I) = CO + X(I) * (C1 + X(I) * (C2 + X(I)
     *                  * (C3 + X(I) * (C4 + X(I) ))))
41034 CONTINUE


C     ELEVEN OPERATIONS - TWO OPERANDS      RATIO = 11/2
      DO 41035 I = 1, N
        Y(I) = CO + X(I) * (C1 + X(I) * (C2 + X(I)
     *                  * (C3 + X(I) * (C4 + X(I)
     *                  * (C5 + X(I)                )))))
41035 CONTINUE


C     THIRTEEN OPERATIONS - TWO OPERANDS      RATIO = 13/2
      DO 41036 I = 1,N
        Y(I) = CO + X(I) * (C1 + X(I) * (C2 + X(I)
     *                  * (C3 + X(I) * (C4 + X(I)
     *                  * (C5 + X(I) * (C6 + X(I) ))))))
41036 CONTINUE


C     FIFTEEN OPERATIONS - TWO OPERANDS      RATIO = 15/2
      DO 41037 I = 1, N
        Y(I) = CO + X(I) * (C1 + X(I) * (C2 + X(I)
     *                  * (C3 + X(I) * (C4 + X(I)
     *                  * (C5 + X(I) * (C6 + X(I)
     *                  * (C7 + X(I)                )))))))
41037 CONTINUE


C     SEVENTEEN OPERATIONS - TWO OPERANDS      RATIO = 17/2
      DO 41038 I = 1, N
        Y(I) = CO + X(I) * (C1 + X(I) * (C2 + X(I)
     *                  * (C3 + X(I) * (C4 + X(I)
     *                  * (C5 + X(I) * (C6 + X(I)
     *                  * (C7 + X(I) * (C8 + X(I) ))))))))
41038 CONTINUE
```

```
C     NINETEEN OPERATIONS - TWO OPERANDS     RATIO = 19/2
      DO 41039 I = 1, N
       Y(I) = CO + X(I) * (C1 + X(I) * (C2 + X(I)
     *                   * (C3 + X(I) * (C4 + X(I)
     *                   * (C5 + X(I) * (C6 + X(I)
     *                   * (C7 + X(I) * (C8 + X(I)
     *                   * (C9 + X(I)                )))))))))
41039 CONTINUE
```

C.3   Group 3: Direct Access with Stride 128

```
      ISTRIDE = 128

C     ONE OPERATION - THREE OPERANDS     RATIO = 1/3
      II = 1
      DO 41060 I = 1, N
       A(II) = B(II) + C(II)
       II = II + ISTRIDE
41060 CONTINUE

C     ONE OPERATION - TWO OPERANDS     RATIO = 1/2
      II =1
      DO 41061 I = 1, N
       A(II) = CO * B(II)
       II = II + ISTRIDE
41061 CONTINUE

C     TWO OPERATIONS - FOUR OPERANDS RATIO = 1/2
      II = 1
      DO 41062 I = 1, N
       A(II) = B(II) * C(II) + D(II)
       II = II + ISTRIDE
41062 CONTINUE

C     THREE OPERATIONS - FIVE OPERANDS     RATIO = 3/5
      II = 1
      DO 41063 I = 1, N
       A(II) = B(II) * C(II) + D(II) * E(II)
       II = II + ISTRIDE
41063 CONTINUE

C     TWO OPERATIONS - THREE OPERANDS     RATIO = 2/3
      II = 1
      DO 41064 I = 1, N
       A(II) = CO * B(II) + C(II)
       II = II + ISTRIDE
41064 CONTINUE

C     TWO OPERATIONS - TWO OPERANDS     RATIO = 1
      II=1
      DO 41070 I = 1, N
       Y(II) = CO + X(II) * C1
       II = II + ISTRIDE
41070 CONTINUE
```

```
C       THREE OPERATIONS - TWO OPERANDS      RATIO = 3/2
        II=1
        DO 41071 I = 1, N
         Y(II) = CO + X(II) * (C1 + X(II) )
         II = II + ISTRIDE
  41071 CONTINUE


C       FIVE OPERATIONS - TWO OPERANDS      RATIO = 5/2
        II=1
        DO 41072 I = 1, N
         Y(II) = CO + X(II) * (C1 + X(II) * (C2 + X(II) ))
         II = II + ISTRIDE
  41072 CONTINUE


C       SEVEN OPERATIONS - TWO OPERANDS      RATIO = 7/2
        II=1
        DO 41073 I = 1, N
         Y(II) = CO + X(II) * (C1 + X(II) * (C2 + X(II)
        *                    * (C3 + X(II)                )))
         II = II + ISTRIDE
  41073 CONTINUE


C       NINE OPERATIONS - TWO OPERANDS      RATIO = 9/2
        II=1
        DO 41074 I = 1, N
         Y(II) = CO + X(II) * (C1 + X(II) * (C2 + X(II)
        *                    * (C3 + X(II) * (C4 + X(II) ))))
         II = II + ISTRIDE
  41074 CONTINUE


C       ELEVEN OPERATIONS - TWO OPERANDS      RATIO = 11/2
        II=1
        DO 41075 I = 1, N
         Y(II) = CO + X(II) * (C1 + X(II) * (C2 + X(II)
        *                    * (C3 + X(II) * (C4 + X(II)
        *                    * (C5 + X(II)                )))))
         II = II + ISTRIDE
  41075 CONTINUE


C       THIRTEEN OPERATIONS - TWO OPERANDS      RATIO = 13/2
        II=1
        DO 41076 I = 1, N
         Y(II) = CO + X(II) * (C1 + X(II) * (C2 + X(II)
        *                    * (C3 + X(II) * (C4 + X(II)
        *                    * (C5 + X(II) * (C6 + X(II) ))))))
         II = II + ISTRIDE
  41076 CONTINUE


C       FIFTEEN OPERATIONS - TWO OPERANDS      RATIO = 15/2
        II=1
        DO 41077 I = 1, N
         Y(II) = CO + X(II) * (C1 + X(II) * (C2 + X(II)
        *                    * (C3 + X(II) * (C4 + X(II)
        *                    * (C5 + X(II) * (C6 + X(II)
        *                    * (C7 + X(II)                )))))))
         II = II + ISTRIDE
  41077 CONTINUE
```

```
C      SEVENTEEN OPERATIONS - TWO OPERANDS      RATIO = 17/2
       II=1
       DO 41078 I = 1, N
        Y(II) = CO + X(II) * (C1 + X(II) * (C2 + X(II)
      *                       * (C3 + X(II) * (C4 + X(II)
      *                       * (C5 + X(II) * (C6 + X(II)
      *                       * (C7 + X(II) * (C8 + X(II) ))))))))
        II = II + ISTRIDE
41078 CONTINUE

C      NINETEEN OPERATIONS - TWO OPERANDS      RATIO = 19/2
       II=1
       DO 41079 I = 1, N
        Y(II) = CO + X(II) * (C1 + X(II) * (C2 + X(II)
      *                       * (C3 + X(II) * (C4 + X(II)
      *                       * (C5 + X(II) * (C6 + X(II)
      *                       * (C7 + X(II) * (C8 + X(II)
      *                       * (C9 + X(II)                )))))))))
        II = II + ISTRIDE
41079 CONTINUE
```

Appendix D

SOLUTIONS TO PROBLEMS

D.1 Chapter 1

1. $\text{RATIO} = \dfrac{(1 - F_V)/S_B + F_V/V_B}{(1 - F_V)/S_A + F_V/V_A}$

2. a. $\text{RATIO} = \dfrac{20}{40 - 39F_V}$

   b. The point at which RATIO $= 1$ or $F_V = 0.51$

3. $\text{RATIO} = \dfrac{(1 - F_P)1/S_B + F_P[1/(S_B \cdot M)]}{(1 - F_P)1/S_A + F_P[1/(S_A \cdot M)]}$

   a. $\text{RATIO} = \dfrac{1024 - 1023F_P}{102.4}$

   b. The point at which RATIO $= 1$ or $F_p = 0.90$
4. a. Machine Y
   b. Machine Z
   c. Define:

$$\text{Perf}(X/Y) = \frac{1}{(1 - F_V)/6 + F_V/60}$$

$$\text{Perf}(X/Z) = \frac{1}{(1 - F_V)/3 + F_V/120}$$

Set the performances equal and solve for F_V to obtain:

$F_V = 0.95$

D.2 Chapter 2

1. Stride	Fetch Time (clock cycles)		
1	$25 + 64$	=	89
2	$25 + 64$	=	89
4	$25 + 64$	=	89
8	$26 + 63 * 2$	=	152

(continued)

Stride	Fetch Time (clock cycles)
16	$26 + 63 * 4 = 278$
32	$26 + 63 * 8 = 530$
64	$26 + 63 * 16 = 1034$
128	$26 + 63 * 32 = 2042$
256	$26 + 63 * 64 = 4058$

2. a. A powerful instruction (vector instruction) that can generate up to 64 results; SIMD

   b. Up to four processors working independently on a single job, so four instructions can be issued each clock cycle; MIMD

   c. Up to four processors using powerful instructions on a single job; MIMD

   d. Each of up to 64 processors executing a single instruction from the CPU; SIMD

   e. A powerful instruction (vector instruction) which can generate up to 32 results; SIMD

   f. Up to 8 processors working independently on a single job; MIMD

   g. Up to 8 processors using vector instructions on a single job; MIMD

3. Time for controlled store under control of a bit vector for a 4-pipe 205 is

$$(51 \times 10000/8)\ 20 \times 10^{-9} \text{ sec}$$

Time for 2-gather periodic, scatter periodic, add is

$$69 + 1.25 \times (10000/S)$$
$$69 + 1.25 \times (10000/S)$$
$$51 + .125 \times (10000/S)$$
$$\underline{71 + 1.25 \times (10000/S)}$$
$$(260 + 38750/S) \times 20 \times 10^{-9} \text{ sec}$$

Set the times equal and solve for S:

$$51 + 1250 = 260 + 38750/S$$
$$S = (38750)/1041 = 37.22$$
or any stride ≥ 38

for a 4-pipe CYBER 205 in 32-bit mode.

For a 2-pipe CYBER 205 in 64-bit mode:

$$51 + 5000 = 260 + 42500/S$$
$$S = (42500)/4791 = 8.87$$
or any stride ≥ 9

4. Time for controlled store:

`B(I)**2`	$(52 + 10000/4) \times 20 \times 10^{-9} \text{ sec}$
`B(I)**2 + C(I)*(1/SCA)`	$(103 + 10000/4) \times 20 \times 10^{-9} \text{ sec}$

$$\text{SQRT (A(I))} \qquad (79 + 10000/.28) \times 20 \times 10^{-9} \text{ sec}$$

$$\text{SQRT (A(I)) * C(I)} \qquad (52 + 10000/4) \times 20 \times 10^{-9} \text{ sec}$$
$$= (286 + 42214) \times 20 \times 10^{-9} \text{ sec}$$

Time for compress/expand approach:

$$\text{COMPRESS B -> TB} \qquad (52 + Z/4) \times 20 \times 10^{-9} \text{ sec}$$

$$\text{COMPRESS C-> TC} \qquad (52 + Z/4) \times 20 \times 10^{-9} \text{ sec}$$

$$\text{TB(I)**2 + TC(I) * (1/SCA) -> TA(I)} \qquad (103 + Z/4) \times 20 \times 10^{-9} \text{ sec}$$

$$\text{EXPAND TA(I) -> A} \qquad (58 + Z/4) \times 20 \times 10^{-9} \text{ sec}$$

$$\text{SQRT (TA(I))} \qquad (79 + Z/.28) \times 20 \times 10^{-9} \text{ sec}$$

$$\text{SQRT (TA(I)) * TC(I) -> TD(I)} \qquad (52 + Z/4) \times 20 \times 10^{-9} \text{ sec}$$

$$\text{EXPAND TD(I) -> D} \qquad (58 + Z/4) \times 20 \times 10^{-9} \text{ sec}$$

$$= (506 + 5.32Z) \times 20 \times 10^{-9} \text{ sec}$$

$(Z = 10000 \times \text{DENSITY},$

where DENSITY is the fraction of elements of B(I).GT.EPSLON)

Set the time equal, and solve for DENSITY:

```
(286 + 42214) = 506 + 5.32 × (10000 * DENSITY)

42500 = 506 + 53200 × DENSITY

DENSITY = 41994/53200 = 79%
```

5. Loop	Cray 1	Cray X − MP	Fujitsu VP200
41020	3 memory	1 memory,+	2 memory
41021	2 memory	1 *	1 memory,*
41022	4 memory	2 memory	2 memory
41023	5 memory	2 memory,*	3 memory
41024	3 memory	1 memory,+,*	2 memory
41030	2 memory	1 +,*	1 memory,+,*
41031	2 memory,+	2 +	2 +
41032	3 +	3 +	3 +
41033	4 +	4 +	4 +
41034	5 +	5 +	5 +
41035	6 +	6 +	6 +
41036	7 +	7 +	7 +
41037	8 +	8 +	8 +
41038	9 +	9 +	9 +
41039	10 +	10 +	10 +

6. Cray-1 performance rates are

a. $\text{flops} = \dfrac{64}{(25 \times 3 \times 64) \times 12.5 \times 10^{-9} \text{ sec}}$

   $\text{flops} = \dfrac{64}{217} \times 80 \times 10^6$

   $\text{Mflops} = \dfrac{64}{217} \times 80 = 23.59$

b. $\text{Mflops} = \dfrac{128}{434} \times 80 = 23.59$

c. $\text{Mflops} = \dfrac{64}{217} \times 80 = 23.59$

d. $\text{Mflops} = \dfrac{128}{409} \times 80 = 25.04$

an improvement factor of 1.06

e. For startup time fifty, the performance rates are

a. $\text{flops} = \dfrac{64}{(50 + 3 \times 64) \times 12.5 \times 10^{-9} \text{ sec}}$

   $\text{flops} = \dfrac{64}{242} \times 80 \times 10^6$

   $\text{Mflops} = \dfrac{64}{242} \times 80 = 21.16$

b. $\text{Mflops} = \dfrac{128}{484} \times 80 = 21.16$

c. $\text{Mflops} = \dfrac{64}{242} \times 80 = 21.16$

d. $\text{Mflops} = \dfrac{128}{434} \times 80 = 23.59$

an improvement factor of 1.11

7. a. $\text{flops} = \dfrac{64}{(45 + 64) \times (8.5 \times 10^{-9} \text{ sec})}$

   $\text{flops} = \dfrac{64}{109} \times 117{,}647{,}059$

   $\text{Mflops} = 69 \text{ Mflops}$

b. $\text{Mflops} = \dfrac{128}{(45 + 64 + 13 + 64)} \times 117.6$

$= \dfrac{128}{186} \times 117.6 = 80.93$

c. $\text{Mflops} = \dfrac{64}{109} \times 117.6 = 69$

d. $\text{Mflops} = \dfrac{128}{(45 + 128)} \times 117.6$

$= \dfrac{128}{173} \times 117.6 = 87.01$

an improvement factor of 1.08

8. Time with conditional vector merge is on the order of $3 \times N$ clock cycles. Time with compressed index is on the order of $5 \times N \times$ (density of truth) clock cycles.

Set times equal, and solve for density:

$3N = 5N \times \text{density}$
$3/5 = \text{density}$

So for density above 60%, conditional vector merge will outperform.

9. Because some compilers cannot vectorize saving the last value of the conditionally defined scalar AB.

D.3 Chapter 3

1. a. No; b. yes; c. no (Just barely, since $4 * 16 = 64$); d. yes; e. no; f. yes (Remember, a stride on the second dimension is multiplied by the first dimension $4 * 8 = 32$.); g. no; h. yes.
2. Loop 20 is not the same as the corresponding array section syntax.
3. Compilers can never detect that the indirect address indexes in IA are unchanging, so they will never treat the reference as an array constant. If A(IA(I)) is only on the left side or only on the right side of the equals sign, it is treated as an array of values. If it is on both sides in the same statement, for example, A(IA(I)) = A(IA(I)) + . . . , then it is treated as a scalar reference to avoid potential recursion.
4. a. A(N) + B(N); b. A(N) + B(N); c. It is difficult to determine the last value of I for which (A(I) .GT. EPS).
5. a. Yes; b. no; c. no. For NEC SX2: a. yes; b. no; c. yes.

D.4 Chapter 4

1. For large values of N, the indirect address will not make much difference, and the times for both loops should be approximately the same.

2.
```
        DO 101  J = 2, N
        VAH(J) = B(J) - B(J-1)
101     CONTINUE

        DO 100  I = 2, N
        DO 100  J = 2, N
        A(I,J) = VAH(J) * A(I-1,J) + C(I,J)
100     CONTINUE

        DO 102  J = 2, N
        VBH(J) = D(J) - D(J-1)
102     CONTINUE

        DO 110  I = N, 2, -1
        DO 110  J = 2, N
        A(I,J) = VBH(J) * A(I-1,J) + C(I,J)
110     CONTINUE
```

3. The average diagonal vector length on an $M \times N$ grid is $(N \times M)/(N + M - 1)$. Given an N-dimensional grid whose dimensions are D_1, $D_2, \ldots, D_N$, then the average number of points on the diagonal planar slices through the grid is:

$$VL_{avg} = \frac{\prod_{i=1}^{N} D_i}{\sum_{i=1}^{N} D_i - N + 1}$$

4. 1a; 2a; 3d; 4b,c; 5b, c; 6d, e; 7d.
5.
```
        DO 44022  I = 2, N
        B       = DELB * (I-1)
        BSC(I) = C(I) * (DELB+C(I) * BSQ(I) - BSQ(I-1) ))
44022   CONTINUE
```

6. `IMAX = ISMAX (N - 1, VSIGABC(2),1)`

`SIGMAX = VSIGABC(IMAX)`

7. The dot-product routine performs much better for larger N.
8. a. Recursion on inner loop; b. Reduction function on inner loop; c. Inner loop has a nonunitary stride, and outer loop is contiguous.
9. `GO TO ( 100,200,300,400,500,600,700,800)NSIZE`

`100 CONTINUE`

`(coding for NSIZE = 1)`

`GO TO 1000`

`200 CONTINUE`

`(coding for NSIZE = 2)`

`. . .`

```
800 CONTINUE
```

```
(coding for NSIZE = 8)
```

```
1000 CONTINUE
```

10. a. Nine; b. Place temporaries in a special common block to be reused in other routines

11. On the Cray X-MP, performance is better for 128 than 64; but we do not want to get too large, since more unnecessary calculations would be done on the strip where A(I).LE.0.0.

12. Vectorized: 8 operations; nonvectorized: 19 operations $8/(8 + 19) = 30\%$

From Amdahl's law:

$$P = 1/(1 - (VS - 1)/VS\ F_v)$$
$$P = 1/(1 - 9/10 \times 8/27)$$
$$P = 1/(1 - 72/270)$$
$$P = (270)/198 = 1.36$$

Additional overhead of extra DO loops will degrade performance a little.

13.

Loop(s)	Explanation
42011	Minimized memory stores
44022	Reduces number of calculations
45013	If IM is larger than KM scalar performance improves, unless on a machine with a cache.
45021, 45022, 45023	Fewer DO loop setups
46012	More calculations overlap
46021	More calculations overlap
46032, 46033, 46034	More calculations overlap
47016	Fewer IFs to test
47029	Fewer IFs to test
47031, 47032, 47033, 47034	Fewer IFs to test
47051	Cleaner code
47091	More regular flow
48021	No function overhead
48061, 48062	Less overhead in calling subroutine once
48021	No overhead in calling subroutine
48031	No overhead in calling subroutine
48052, 48054	Less overhead in calling subroutine
48081, 48082	Less overhead in calling subroutine twice instead of 2 * N
48091	No overhead in calling subroutine

INDEX

215